DATE DUE

P9-APJ-167

challenge to reason

challenge

to

reason

C. WEST CHURCHMAN
University of California, Berkeley

McGRAW-HILL BOOK COMPANY

New York   San Francisco   St. Louis   Toronto   London   Sydney

Copyright © 1968 by McGraw-Hill, Inc. All rights reserved.
No part of this publication may be reproduced,
stored in a retrieval system, or transmitted,
in any form or by any means, electronic, mechanical,
photocopying, recording, or otherwise, without the
prior written permission of the publisher.
Printed in the United States of America.

Library of Congress catalog card number: 68-13513

1234567890 PECZ 7543210698

HD
38
C47

Aa195c68

preface

I first began thinking seriously about the theme of this book after undertaking a longer project to study "the design of inquiring systems." Instead of just asking the traditional question of how human minds come to learn from experience, this study asked how one could design a system that would learn from its experience in some "optimal" fashion. My plan was to translate some of the historical texts in the theory of knowledge into modern systems terminology, by assuming that the authors were discussing the components of a system design. As I was working over Leibniz's *Monadology* I was struck again by the fact that in his approach to the inquiring system he was insisting that a concept of the whole system was essential in understanding how each "part" worked. This, of course, was a very common piece of sense, but in the context of inquiry its implications were not so obvious. What Leibniz and other "designers" of the seventeenth century were claiming was that the inquiring system needed some guarantor—a God—in the management of its affairs, else sound control of the process was impossible. Now in these days of rather intense study of systems and their management, few seem in the least concerned about such a guarantor, or indeed about the characteristics of the whole system in any but a very narrow sense. If Leibniz was right, then modern theories of system design and managerial control are sadly lacking in their reasoning. If Leibniz was wrong, we 'must know enough about the whole system to be able to show that no guarantor is needed. This is the "challenge to reason" that confronts us.

Much of this book was written while I was working on research sponsored by the National Aeronautics and Space Administration. NASA, under the wise guidance of its administrator James Webb, has given general grants to several universities to study both the management and the social impact of research and technology. At Berkeley, a social science group in the Space Sciences Laboratory was formed. Some chapters of this book were reviewed by this group and by NASA personnel. I am grateful for all the comments and criticisms I received from both sources, and especially for comments from Professor Samuel Silver, the director of the Space Sciences Laboratory. I am also grateful for the comments of Professor Thomas A. Cowan, Dr. Frederick Betz, Dr. Ian Mitroff, Professor Philburn Ratoosh, Professor Paul Lieber, and Dr. Helmut Krauch of Heidelberg, Germany, all of whom discussed the topic of the book extensively with me. The last named and I have been experimenting on the "dialectic" mode of presenting management issues, a mode discussed at various points in this book.

The chapters in Part II were originally presented as lectures, or contributed to other volumes, as follows:

Chapter seven, "Rational Decision Making," was given at the joint Canadian Operational Research Society and The Institute of Management Sciences (TIMS) meetings in Toronto, May, 1962, and appeared in *Management Technology*, October, 1962.

Chapter eight, "The X of X," was given at the Ninth Annual International meeting of TIMS, Ann Arbor, Michigan, September, 1962, and appeared in *Management Science*, vol. 9, no. 3, April, 1963.

Chapter nine, "Science and God," was given at the Operations Research Society of America meetings under the title of "The Art of the State" in Washington, D.C., May, 1962.

Chapter ten, "Theoretical Management," appeared under the title of "Marketing Theory as Marketing Management" in S. J. Shapiro, (ed.), *Theory in Marketing*, 2d ed., University of Pennsylvania Press, Philadelphia.

Chapter eleven, "The Heroism of Applied Science," was a paper delivered at the Department of Defense Logistics Research Conference in Airlie House, Warrenton, Virginia, May, 1965.

Chapter twelve, "The Humor of Science," was given at the New York Chapter of TIMS in May, 1965 under the title of "The Humor of Management Science."

Chapter thirteen, "Large Models of Systems," was presented at the Second Stony Brook Conference on Advances in Computing, Stony Brook, New York, June, 1966.

The poem on page 134 is from Dylan Thomas' "Collected Poems," copyright 1946 by Dylan Thomas; reprinted by permission of New Directions Publishing Corporation.

Permission to quote has been generously granted by the journals *Management Science* and *Management Technology*, and by the University of Pennsylvania Press.

The topic of the book is an extension of a lifetime's work with Professor Russell L. Ackoff, though he is not responsible for the particular direction of intellectual adventure that this book takes. Many of the ideas contained in this book were discussed most fruitfully with Sebastian B. Littauer, David B. Hertz, J. S. Minas, and Al H. Schainblatt.

As always, I enjoy the patience and thorough care of Alice Tabet and the craftsmanship and attention of Phyllis Dexter.

C. WEST CHURCHMAN

for

TOM COWAN

who tells the best stories of all

part I | science
and
management

the challenge
of improvement

Man is an animal that can complain and praise, and frequently does both. He believes that the world he lives in can be described in terms of better and worse, in terms of good and evil, in terms of excellence and incompetence.

Man is also one of those animals who lives in a system, that is, in an environment, various aspects of which are interrelated, and in which the whole complex of the interrelated parts is supposed to serve his fundamental purposes.

How can the systems in which man lives be characterized in terms of better and worse, good and evil, excellence and incompetence? By what reasoning do we come to believe that one nation is a better "system" than another nation? Or, at a more mundane level, how do we reason that one traffic system, for example, air transportation, can be regarded as "better" than the old-fashioned system of horse-drawn vehicles?

Not only do we assume that one system can be meaningfully regarded as better than another system, but in our praising and complaining we also assume that we can actually do something to improve the systems that we inhabit. Of course, this very important assumption is not one that all men will willingly accept. Many present-day philosophers believe that our technological systems are more or less determined and that their particular destructive effects on man will happen, whatever we do to change them. Yet most of us would not be inclined to arrive at so pessimistic a conclusion concerning our fate until we had tried to explore the more attractive assmuption that we have a certain inherent ability to change the world for the better; else how can we justify our complaining and praising?

Thus we wish to explore the assumption that man may consciously review the possibilities of change of his systems, and, in the light of his concept of improvement and deterioration, he can willingly select among the choices available to him.

If we do assume that we have the capability of improving systems, then what do we mean by "improvement"? Much has been said on the meaning of this concept. Ever since the earliest days of intellectual history, philosophers have paid special attention to the ideas of good and bad, or right and wrong, in the arena of human conduct.

Despite these historical explorations, however, men have neglected a very serious problem in defining the concept of improvement. The problem is very simple: How can we design improvement in large systems without understanding the whole system, and if the answer is that we cannot, how is it possible to understand the whole system?

This problem, as I say, has not occupied the thoughts of many philosophers. It is only natural to expect that improvement can occur in certain sectors of the system without our having delved deeply into the characteristics of the whole system. Thus, for example, there is a tradition in Western thought that parts of the whole system can be studied and improved more or less in isolation from the rest of the system.

So deeply ingrained is this concept of social improvement in Western thought that we naturally think it proper to subdivide our society into functional elements. We think it proper that each element develop its own criteria of improvement and that the elements be as free as possible from the interference of the other parts of the social structure.

Consider, for example, two aspects of modern society about which Western man expresses a good deal of pride: education and health. In both these areas, surely, there has been a decided improvement over the last few decades. In education, more people reach higher grades before terminating their formal education, the materials presented are far more sophisticated, and the general level of knowledge of the student in many cases is far superior to that of even two or three decades ago. In the area of health, more people survive to a later age, more people live lives in a less painful fashion, more cures are effective and permit people to function in normal ways, than has ever happened before in the human race. Surely it is reasonable to say that improvement has occurred in both education and health during the past few decades. Why can't we simply say that society is to be divided into sectors, like education and health, and that appropriate measures of improvement are to be developed in each sector without requiring any deep analysis or broad perspective of the whole system of which these sectors are a part?

But are these so-called improvements in health and education really improvements? For example, it is commonplace for many critics of our current society to point out the serious deficiencies of our educational system. These criticisms show that educational systems are often very routine, that students are forced to follow rigid patterns of thought, that creative potential is lost, and that people often lead dull, uninteresting lives simply because of the unimaginative educational training they have received in their earliest years.

The same remarks apply equally well to health. Of course the system of today that assists men in attaining more healthy lives is an improvement over some systems, but in many respects it ignores or puts too little emphasis on very important aspects of the healthy life of the adult human being. For example, there is much to be said for the idea that the health policy of the past few decades has paid far too little attention to mental health or to the general problems of the development of the adult human being, so that many persons spend what must be regarded as healthy but stupid lives. Consequently one may question whether or not the measurement of the improvement of health in terms of the average span of the human life is an appropriate way to consider the concept of improvement.

If human lives are increased in length but made far less interesting, then has a real improvement in health occurred?

These are the obvious objections that occur to any reasonable man when claims are made about improvement in specific sectors of human society. However, an even deeper problem will occupy our attention in subsequent pages of this chapter: Even granting that improvements in education and health have occurred, what has been the sacrifice that men have made to attain these improvements? More specifically, given the resources available to us to improve our systems, could these resources have been used in a far better way than they were used in the development of health and education? If, instead of using our limited resources as we did, we had used them in some other way that would effect far greater improvements, then we would have to say that, whatever the advantages we have gained from health and education, they have been gained at a most unsatisfactory sacrifice of our limited resources.

Furthermore, and this is very much to the point, the so-called resources available to health and education were not just the resources that were in fact allocated by our society to these two sectors. Some decision was made to allocate to these sectors from the resources that the whole system had at its disposal; the question we are raising about the concept of improvement is whether the resources that in fact were made available to the administrators of education and health were correct. Perhaps we should have allocated far greater or far fewer resources to these specific activities.

But to pose the problem of improvement of health and education in this manner is to ask a question about the entire system of our resources. That is, we must ask a question about the whole system to be able to judge the improvement of a segment of the system. Hence we seem forced to conclude that anyone who actually believes in the possibility of improving systems is faced with the problem of understanding the properties of the whole system, and that he cannot concentrate his attention merely on one sector.

The problem of system improvement is the problem of the "ethics of the whole system." In some sense this use of the term *ethics* may seem unusual, because ethics is a term often used to connote concepts of good and bad with respect to individual conduct. Indeed, in ordinary discourse the basic underlying notion behind discussions of ethics is closely related to blame and praise. Yet it seems futile indeed to blame the entire system for its particular inept behavior; instead we have a natural inclination to try to single out individuals within systems who should be blamed for the particular evils or inefficiencies these systems exhibit.

Now of course the discussion of individual behavior does properly belong under the theme described here as the ethics of large-scale systems. It is perfectly proper to talk about a given person within a system in terms of the quality of his behavior, just as we have talked about the quality of behavior of education and health. We could therefore sensibly ask whether an individual might have lived his life in a better way than he did, given the resources made available to him by the whole system. The point, however, is that we cannot judge improvement in an individual unless we have some understanding of the nature of the whole system in which this individual lives. The theme we are exploring is one that claims that a concept of ethical conduct depends at least in part on the concept of system improvement. The ethics of whole systems incorporates the concepts of the ethics of individual behavior and places the problem of the ethics of individual behavior within the context of the whole system.

What has just been said may not appear to be sound common sense. After all, many of us feel that an individual man or a group of men may have the qualities of excellence in ethical conduct, and that these qualities can be exhibited independent of considerations of the whole system in which these men live their lives. The great saints and lovers, the great political leaders and scientists—indeed, all the "greats" of our heritage—exhibited these qualities of excellence even though the whole system had many characteristics of evil and deterioration. And yet, whatever common sense may say, reason in its insistence on having an adequate understanding must conclude that the illustrations of ethical excellence so often recorded in our histories simply lack any clear evidence that the lives of these great men were indeed ethically excellent. Given their endowments and the resources of their society, how can we adequately satisfy ourselves that their lives might not have been lived in a far better fashion, or indeed that the acts these men exhibited really were acts of improvement with respect to their systems?

Furthermore, the problem of judging ethical excellence in the light of reason is even more difficult, as we have seen. We use the phrase *given the resources* available to the individual or to the sector of society. Yet the resources themselves are a creation of society and we can ask ourselves whether the resources might not have been entirely different from the ones that were made available. In our modern society we make various kinds of resources, such as telephones, airplanes, and appliances, available to certain individuals. We can well ask ourselves whether the particular resources that this society produces are not entirely inappropriate to the well-being of our society. We must understand not only what the entire system is like, but what the entire system might be like if men exhibited greater enlightenment than they typically do.

Well, let us accept reason's demand that we must understand the aspects of the entire system before we can create improvement in sectors of the system. Does it follow that system improvement is an impossibility? Of course not. Suppose for the moment we explore some fascinating developments in man's attempts to improve systems. Modern efforts to improve man's systems are part of the great tradition of the struggle of men to create a better world for human life, namely the use of knowledge in system improvement. To what extent can man successfully use what he has learned about himself and the natural world to redesign systems in order to improve them? Can science be successfully applied to system redesign? The answer of the last two decades has been that it can, and that the various disciplines of science can be successfully applied to the study of system improvement. Of particular importance in this regard have been the developments occurring in applied mathematics and computer technology.

If a scientist looks at a system and asks whether it can be improved, it is only natural for him to demand a more precise definition of "improvement." He wishes to make this concept of improvement sufficiently precise in order to develop empirical measures of improvement and thus translate the data that he collects into criteria of better or worse with respect to the system that he is examining. This notion of developing empirical measures of improvement was discussed at length by Jeremy Bentham, over a century and a half ago. Bentham proposed that we should translate human experience into meaningful measures of better and worse by use of what he called *pleasure-pain* calculus. In general terms, his idea was that a national system improves to the extent that it creates more pleasure *on the whole* for the members of society. Bentham was well aware of the great difficulties of translating the simple experiences of pleasure and pain into any kind of meaningful social measure. For example, something as elusive as pleasure disappears and is often counteracted by certain kinds of painful experience. In addition, Bentham recognized what modern scientists of system design also recognize, namely, that uncertainties have to be introduced. He also noted that one must determine whether improvements introduced in one sector properly compensate for deficiencies brought about in other sectors of the system.

Instead of trying to use pleasure or general welfare, the scientist may conclude that a system can be judged by its financial status, as so frequently happens in the case of our industrial corporations. Here the scientific approach will develop measures of improvement in terms of money. Thus in Western free competitive society many sectors of the society are judged according to their net profit, or return, to shareholders.

Assume for the moment that some reasonable measures of better and worse with respect to systems can be developed by the scientist. His next task is to translate a physical description of a system into a measure of system performance. The physical status of the system may be the empirical description of the system's ability to do various things as described by physically observable events. The scientist has a remarkable ability to describe the physical world, and he uses this ability as his starting point. Mathematics then enables him to translate the physical description into a measure of effectiveness of the whole system. The mathematical function he uses is one in which the effectiveness of the whole system becomes the dependent variable, and the various relevant physical characteristics of the system become the independent variables. Consequently the scientist is able to say that *if* the system has such-and-such a physical description, then (as demonstrated by his mathematical formula) it has such-and-such a measure of system effectiveness.

Next the scientist will recognize that some physical characteristics of the system can be changed, that is, that some characteristics of the physical system are in the control of various people who live in the system. For example, the manager of an airline may be able to change the number of planes available at a given airport on a given morning, or the manager of an industrial plant may be able to change the number of personnel working in a given area of his plant, or the administrator of a school may change the number of teachers who teach a given subject in a given semester. Just because the physical characteristics of the system are related by means of a mathematical function to the effectiveness of the system, the scientist will be able to judge whether a system change results in a system improvement.

Of course the manager of a system in some way recognizes this point as well, but the reason why he may fail in many cases to change the system in the direction of improvement is that he fails to recognize the complex relationship between the physical characteristics and the effectiveness of the system. For example, if the manager or administrator changes a physical part of the system, the change will often cause changes in other parts of the system. These very subtle effects of his decisions may not be obvious to him and yet may very well be captured by a careful scientific study of the sort just described. The scientist might find that if the manager of an airline system had three or four more planes available at a given airport at a certain time, this would result in a system improvement even though it meant depriving other parts of the system of aircraft. Similarly he might find that the administrator of a school could improve the entire system by using more teachers to teach a given course even though this meant a sacrifice of teaching resources in other parts of the curriculum.

The analogy with medical science may be of use here. Most of us have an ability to make choices that preserve our health. Yet we frequently find ourselves in positions where, because of our lack of training, we cannot understand the consequences of our decisions. In such cases we go to a *scientist*, namely, the medical doctor, who can then develop a relationship between our physical condition and certain measures of improvement in our bodily health.

It is very exciting to contemplate the possibilities of using science to study the improvement of large-scale systems. Such investigations suggest to the young creative mind a career in which he uses his intellectual attainments in the direct improvement of human systems. Human systems are as subtle and difficult to study as any aspect of the natural world. This point can perhaps be best understood when one realizes the enormous number of pathways to system improvement that are available to systems managers. Normally the human mind is only capable of considering a very small number of these possible pathways.

All of us are managers of some kind of system. It is also true that each one of us tries to translate the physical description of his environment into various criteria of better and worse. For example, if there is dirt on the kitchen floor, which is a physical description, this is translated into a fairly serious measure of the deficiency of the home system; the home owner then sees that, with the utilization of the resources at his control, he can improve the system by allocating his resources to cleaning up the mess. In this case the home owner scans only a very limited number of possibilities. He can either ignore the dirt on the floor or take a broom to it.

In the case of larger systems, the number of possible choices open to the manager of the system becomes very great. There are many ways in which the industrial firm can produce its items and many ways in which it can distribute them on the market. There are many ways in which an individual school can be run; there are many ways in which a traffic system can be designed; and so on. It is only natural for the scientist to search in his own educational background for ways in which he can reduce the complexity of system choices to a manageable form. He often does this by means of mathematical tools. As soon as he begins to use his mathematical knowledge, then we can say that the knowledge he is applying goes beyond the available knowledge of the average manager. That is, the scientist would be able to apply knowledge that the manager or administrator is unaware of, and the scientist will do this to create system improvement. If we return to our previous analogy, much the same thing happens when a doctor examines a patient. Most people recognize that they can improve their bodily systems by keeping clean and following a certain type of diet, but they are often incapable of understanding how to improve the system when certain events occur leading to various kinds of deterioration of the body. In such cases the number of possible alternatives are very great indeed; the doctor applies his science to reduce the number of possibilities to the ones that are clearly appropriate. And the patient does not expect that the science being applied to his improvement is one that he himself can acquire or even understand.

In the modern age we are thus coming to recognize a relationship of great importance between the scientist and the human being who lives in the systems created by man. The scientist may become a kind of doctor of systems, that is, someone capable of using his knowledge to develop system improvement. This knowledge cannot be understood by the average person, or even by the people who normally manage the system.

The idea that scientific disciplines may be able to cast light on methods of system improvement was realized in the 1940s in Great Britain during the Battle of Britain, and later on in the United States when the military managers began using scientific resources to study various critical problems of defense systems. These efforts earlier went under the name *operations research* and more recently under such names as *management science, system science,* etc. So successful were these efforts that they were enormously increased after the war and have now become an established part of military organizations in many countries. The scientist uses his own training and educational background to try to study the nature of military systems, to translate the physical description of a defense system into concepts of improvement. He then recommends to managers of the defense system various ways in which improvement may occur.

The advent of the large-scale computer has also opened new avenues of approach to system improvement. In many cases the physical description of even a fairly simple system involves thousands of variables, and the mathematical relationship holding between these variables may be very complicated. Two decades ago, even though the scientist might in theory be able to describe a system and translate its description into measures of improvement, he could not feasibly accomplish the task because of the complexity of the mathematical relationships. Mathematics as a discipline has had its own development and has often ignored certain types of "messy" mathematical problems, because from a mathematical point of view they represent very little challenge, no matter how useful they may be in their application. The computer, however, is extremely adept at handling a large number of variables and performing computational feats to arrive at a meaningful conclusion, and presumably never becomes bored.

Today around the world there are thousands of scientists and engineers who devote their lives to the study of systems and their improvement. They try to develop very careful physical descriptions of systems, and they try to translate these physical descriptions into mathematical "models" which enable them to predict what will happen if certain changes are initiated in the systems. These efforts are really extensions of earlier efforts in engineering and economics. Indeed, the applied economist has always regarded himself as someone who tries to assist the manager in the improvement of systems, just as the engineer has typically taken a segment of a system and tried to apply his knowledge of physics or chemistry to create system improvement.

Nevertheless, the trend of the last decade has introduced a new relationship between scientist and manager, because now the scientist is working much closer to those who are directly concerned with the responsibility of system performance. In the past the economist or engineer could say to himself, "These are the goals that my client wishes to attain, and I will study how he can best attain them. It is none of my business whether these goals are the correct ones." But when the scientist begins to work hand in hand with the top administrator, he can no longer take such a detached viewpoint toward his client's goals. He must ask himself whether the goals specified by the client are the correct ones in terms of the client's interests, and he often discovers that they are incorrectly stated or dangerously narrow from the point of view of the improvement of the entire system.

The operations researcher has in fact introduced a term, *suboptimization*, to characterize the dangers of too narrow a perspective of system improvement. Through experience he has become aware that managers and other members of human systems have a tendency now and then to become alarmed at the performance of one aspect of the system. Thus the manager of an industrial corporation may be frightened at the increased size of the inventories he is carrying in stock. Or the manager of an urban community may become alarmed at the traffic congestion in certain areas. Or the educational administrator may become alarmed at the increased size of classes. The public press, in its efforts to keep its readership, often tries to arouse the public by pointing out deficiencies in one sector of society, for example, juvenile delinquency, threats to our national security, and so on. In all these cases the natural tendency on the part of the system inhabitants is to try to remove the difficulty immediately. The industrial manager tries to cut back on inventory, the city manager seeks to widen the streets at a given intersection, the educational administrator attempts to find more teachers for the overloaded courses, the public reacts by writing to its Congressmen recommending "direct action." In all these cases, however, a kind of "system pathology" may be observed, because, in the attempt to overcome the symptoms of trouble, the managers may swing the system into an even more dangerous situation. Cutting back on inventories may produce critical shortages, and customers may become so dissatisfied as to give up their patronage altogether. If a street intersection is widened at one point, the traffic patterns in neighboring parts of the city may become overly congested. By increasing the number of teachers that teach a given course, the administrator may ignore the fact that the course has become obso-/ lescent. By taking direct action, the legislators may very well bring harm upon a large number of innocent people. The operations researcher therefore feels that a very important part of his role is to prevent unsatisfactory suboptimization. He believes that his responsibility is not merely to translate what the client *says* his needs are but to study these needs in relation to the broader aims of the client.

Naturally many people will feel that the scientist has taken on a very dangerous role. Indeed, the astute reader must long ago have felt that in the remarks of this chapter there is a certain underlying implication that is most dangerous, especially to the Western individualistic and democratic mind. This is the implication that man, in improving his systems, may undertake to *plan* them. Operations research seems to be saying to us that via science we can introduce certain types of social planning which will influence the lives of all men without permitting them the freedom to object or to change the decisions. The idea seems to come dangerously close to Eastern communism as opposed to Western democracy.

To the Western mind it often appears that the Communist is someone who wishes to centralize social planning and place it in the hands of an "elite," who will then dictate the characteristics of the whole system and decide what is best for each member of the system. Of course, to the Eastern Communist mind, it appears as though Western democracy has adopted an unsatisfactory notion of system improvement because it hands over the design of social systems to certain individuals who manipulate the system to best serve their own interests and to the detriment of the rest of society.

So terrible has been the thought of the totalitarian society to many Western minds that even the fairly modest attempts by the scientist to assist the manager and politician in making social decisions are taken to lean in the direction of a dictatorial state. If the scientist begins to move next to the top administrator, it appears as though the scientific community is threatening to "take over" the centralized planning of society. To many it appears that what will occur is a form of totalitarian enterprise in which anyone who can convince the rest that he is a "scientist" can sit in the middle of the web and dictate the behavior of the people in the rest of system. This is a threat, of course, as everyone well recognizes, because it is always possible for a man with sufficient power to claim that he also has the science to justify his use of the power. Indeed, this is the typical action on the part of diplomats who claim to have a superior knowledge with respect to certain other countries. Thus Western democracies sometimes invade other countries to "prevent the growth of centralized power," claiming that they have superior knowledge about the threats to the country, but thereby going against the very principle that justifies their invasion.

In some sense this whole discussion of centralized planning by a power elite versus democratic planning is irrelevant to the issue of the role of the scientist in assisting national, local, industrial, and other types of managers. The freedom of individuals to make choices based on their own wills and perspectives is a freedom that has a value of its own within the system and should be permitted to occur. Wherever centralized planning begins to narrow the ability of individuals to express themselves in certain traditional ways, then the system has become *less* effective and the system scientist should translate the lack of freedom in the system into a deterioration of the system effectiveness.

In another sense, the question is of considerable importance and is an excellent illustration of the theme already introduced into our discussion. The fundamental systems question is: Where in the total human system should freedom of choice be permitted for the inhabitants of the system? We have come to learn that people should not be permitted to set fires wherever they wish, to acquire property whenever they feel so inclined, to drive their automobiles in any direction or at any speed their human spirit indicates. To permit any of these "freedoms" is to make the systems worse, given the present mental development of the human race: Too many people would express their free spirits in ways disastrous to the coinhabitants of the human systems. In understanding and evaluating the concept of freedom in our society it is necessary to look at the way in which permission of individuals to make free choices disturbs the rest of the social system. And since each individual is in effect a "sector" of society, we are asking the same question we asked earlier—whether "sector improvement" can occur without due regard to the characteristics of the whole system. And since it cannot, that is, since it is essential to understand the ethics of the whole system in order to develop concepts of excellence and improvement in the sector, we are obliged to say that the ethical norm of freedom depends on our ability to understand the whole system.

There is another way to say the same thing, with an equally puzzling conclusion. We have talked of the scientist as though he were the servant of a client, and we have discussed how the scientist may try to come to understand the real needs of his client. But why should the scientist have such a servant-master relationship to his client? Isn't the scientist obliged to go beyond his client's needs and ask whether these needs are morally correct ones? We should be able to criticize an applied scientist because he serves the needs of an organization whose goals are socially detrimental. Consequently, the scientist in entering into a relationship with a client seems obliged to ask how the client's own activities fit into the whole system so that he, the scientist, may judge whether his service to the client is a proper one.

And this brings us back to the same theme: The Ethics of Whole Systems. We are talking not about techniques of improving performance *given* the goals that certain people wish to attain. We are also talking about whether the goals themselves are proper ones, and we are asking how the scientist can possibly come to answer this question. The underlying theme is that if he fails to answer the question, he fails to "apply knowledge to system improvement."

The seriousness of the issues we are to consider here seems to become emphatic every time we look at the activities of the playground. The playground is a system of people who will inherit the kind of system we are creating today, and the natural inclination of all of us to be parents, whether biological or simply organizational, makes us realize that the kinds of things that we fondly regard as "improvements" may impose upon the coming generations of men the most horrible forms of social living, or else the most delightful.

How is it possible to judge systems without looking at the consequences of our system changes to the generations to come? Of all the principles of ethics that men have been able to devise, none is so fundamental as the ethical postulate that we are morally obliged to meet the demands that coming generations would have imposed upon us were they able to speak to us today.

In the context of the problem of large systems that include not only the world of today but also of tomorrow, it is clear that no person or group of persons—scientist, politician, or whatever—can honestly say that he understands enough to guarantee by his decisions and recommendations an improvement of even a small sector of society. We are all suboptimizers, perhaps prone to the most dangerous kinds of suboptimization. Can we hope to find a rational way of improving our lives?

the myth
of management

Making decisions is, on the one hand, one of the most fascinating manifestations of biological activity and, on the other hand, a matter of terrifying implications for the whole of the human race. Although this activity is both fascinating and awesome, it is difficult to find a satisfactory name for it in any of the common languages. In English we use such terms as *manager, administrator, executive,* or simply *decision maker.* Yet each of these terms fails somehow to capture the true significance of this important activity of the human being. Because we need a label to conduct our discussion, I shall risk choosing the term *manager* and begin to say some things that will generalize on this term beyond its ordinary usage in English.

The manager is the man who decides among alternative choices. He must decide which choice he believes will lead to a certain desired objective or set of objectives. But his decision is not an abstract one, because it creates a type of reality. The manager is the man with the magic that enables him to create in the world a state of affairs that would not have occurred except for him. We say that the manager is one who has the authority to make such choices. He is also a person who has the responsibility for the choices he has made in the sense that the rest of his fellow men may judge whether he should be rewarded or punished for his choices; he is the person who justifiably is the object of praise or blame.

So broad a description of the manager makes managers of us all. It is a common failing of the labels that language applies to things that they may be generalized to encompass everything, as philosopers have long recognized in the case of such labels as *matter* and *mind*. It takes no great sophomoric talent to see that the world is basically matter and that everything could be reduced thereto. Nor does it take any great astuteness to see that everything a human being recognizes as natural reality is the product of some mind or collection of minds. So, too, the label *manager* may become appropriately applied to practically everything or at least to every human, once we describe the manager as someone having the authority and responsibility for making choices. I am interested in the broad aspects of decision making, but for present purposes I want to add one more stipulation that makes the label *manager* less general. This is the stipulation that managerial activity take place within a "system": The manager must concern himself with interrelated parts of a complex organization of activities, and he is responsible for the effectiveness of the whole system in the manner discussed in the last chapter.

But even this further stipulation concerning the use of the label *manager* permits us to describe many activities as management. It is true that in the history of England and the United States, the term *management* has often been narrowed to mean the managing of industrial activities, especially for the purpose of generating profit for an enterprise. In this connection management is contrasted with labor. In government activities our use of the term *manager* is often labelled *administrator*, and the term *executive* is often used to describe people who are given the legal authority to put into practice the laws of the land. All these activities, whether they be at the level of government or industry or education or health, or whatever, have a common ground which we wish to explore. The common ground is the burden of making choices about system improvement and the responsibility of responding to the choices made in a human environment in which there is bound to be opposition to what the manager has decided. Thus the head of a labor union, the state legislator, the head of a government agency, the foreman of a shop are all managers in our sense. So is a man in his own family a manager; so is the captain of a football team. Probably all of us at some time or other in our lives become managers when, because of appointment to a committee or because of our political activities, we take on the authority and responsibility of making decisions in complex systems. Managing is an activity of which we are all aware, and its consequences concern each one of us.

I said that managers must bear the burden of the decisions they make. I could have added, in a more optimistic tone, that they enjoy the pleasures accompanying the power to make decisions. And certainly many managers in today's society do find a great deal of psychic satisfaction in the roles they play which society so clearly recognizes as important and which it credits with a great deal of prestige.

Now managing is a type of behavior, and since it's a very important type of behavior, you might expect that we know a great deal about it. But we don't at all. We could also explore the many ways in which managers often think they know how they manage, but observers of their behavior often differ from them quite radically. The manager is frequently astonished to hear a sociologist's description of his activities, which he believes he himself knows so well, and he resents the inclination on the part of the "detached" scientist to try to describe the activity that he performs.

Imagine an observer carefully trained to study such activities as bees in a hive, or fish in a school, or birds in a flock, and suppose such a student of nature becomes curious about the behavior of judges during a trial. How might such a scientist describe what the judge actually does? He might learn a little bit from some of the reflective judges, and perhaps a little bit more from the sociologists and other scientists who have attempted to describe legal behavior, but he would find that most of the activity remains a huge mystery to the whole of humanity—a mystery that no one has ever felt inclined to investigate in detail.

The whole activity of managing, important as it is for the human race, is still largely an unknown aspect of the natural world. When man detaches himself and tries to observe what kind of living animal he is, he finds that he knows very little about the things most important to him and precious little about his role as a decision maker. Few managers are capable of describing how they reach their decisions in a way that someone else can understand; few can tell us how they feel about the decisions once they have been made. Of course, despite our ignorance about managerial phenomena, a great deal is written on the subject in popular magazines and managerial journals. It appears that the less we know about a subject, the more we are inclined to write extensively about it with great conviction. Some writings describe the various rituals followed in organizations prior and posterior to the actual managerial decision. But most of these descriptions pay little attention to the very puzzling question of *when* a decision actually occurred and *who* made it. A great deal is said about committee deliberations and other aspects of organizational rationality that go into the making of a decision, and the many checks and controls that are exerted to determine whether the decisions have been made properly. Much attention is paid to these aspects of organizational decision making, because they show up on the surface, so to speak. But the facts that a committee deliberated for three hours and then a decision emerged do not tell us *who* made the decision, *how* it was made, or *when* it was made. It might be added that the verbal assertions of the committee often do not tell us *what* decision is made.

So there is a great mystery of the natural world: the *who, when, how,* and *what* of man's decision making.

But even if we were to succeed in discovering a great deal more than we have about management, the result would be at best descriptive. It would be merely the background of the basic problem before us, namely, the question of how the manager *should* decide.

Am I right in claiming that we know so little about management? After all, most of us are quite willing, even eager, to express an opinion about managers, because we love to praise and complain. We don't hesitate to say that some men are better managers than others. We are constantly criticizing our political leaders. Biographers are accustomed to choose the most "outstanding" leaders of the age as the subject of their texts. These leaders may be great political leaders, leaders of industry, leaders of social movements, of religion, and so on. What is the quality these men of success have that their less successful colleagues lack? Since we believe we can identify "successful" leaders, surely we also believe we know a great deal about what a manager *should* decide. For example, in the case of the Presidents of the United States, we are told in our schoolboy texts that we can readily recognize that some of these Presidents were "great" and some of them far from great. What is the quality of greatness that we are led to ascribe to some of these Presidents?

A ready answer is at hand—the successful and great Presidents were those who made decisions that today we clearly recognize to be correct, and those who made these decisions in the face of severe opposition. We are led to believe that the activity of great Presidents is a mavelous example of successful decision making in large complex systems.

But the sceptics among us will find this answer quite unsatisfactory as an explanation of what constitutes greatness in a President. In the first place, history has no record of what would have happened had the opposition's point of view succeeded or if serious modifications had been made in the choices of the so-called great Presidents. What if the Union had *not* been saved, or our independence declared? History seems only to have recorded the episodes that followed upon the particular decision that was made and does not provide us with an analysis of events that might have occurred if an alternative had been adopted.

More curious still is the implicit assumption that a successful President made his great decisions on the basis of his own particular abilities. Since evidence is so often lacking that great Presidents of the past had these abilities, there is a natural inclination on the part of many of us to ascribe either determinism or randomness to the activities of so-called successful managers. In the case of determinism, we might argue that the events of the world occur by the accidental conglomeration of many forces unknown to man, and that these forces produce "decisions" that man in his innocence believes that he himself makes. The decision of independence in 1776 was, according to this view, simply the outgrowth of many complex human and physical interrelationships. Those who adopt the idea of randomness simply add to the physical determinism of events a random fluctuation of the sort occurring in a roulette wheel or in the shuffling of cards. They would then be willing to admit that other decisions might have been made in 1776 or later, but that these decisions would be very much like the outcome of another spin of the roulette wheel. In either event, whether we choose to describe the world of decision-making as determinism or as randomness, we conclude that ascribing greatness to the decision makers in Independence Hall would be a mistake unless one meant by greatness some recognizable features of the determined or random events occurring in the world. By analogy one might say that the man who spins the roulette wheel is its "manager" who decides nothing about the outcome of his spins; a multitude of hidden physical forces determine where the wheel will stop. Calling a President great is like calling the spinner of a roulette wheel that happens to have a satisfactory result a great spinner.

This is certainly a crass and impolite way to describe the great managerial minds of the past. Surely we can do more for their memories than to describe them as irrelevant aspects of the history of society. We might try to look into the story of their lives to find evidence that they really had superior methods of deliberation. We might try to show that they had the sort of brilliance and courage that creates an ability to handle confusing pieces of information and to reach appropriate decisions. Perhaps the great manager is an extremely adept information processor who can act so rapidly that he himself is not even aware of the comparisons and computations he has made.

Indeed, this last is more or less the popular image of the great manager. For example, many scientists who advise politicians, corporate managers, and other decision makers often state that they cannot possibly attempt to tell such men what decisions *should* be made. At best they believe they can merely tell the decision maker about certain outcomes if the decisions are adopted. Thus the more modest among the advisers believe that they have no intent of "re-placing" the managers they advise. And yet if these scientific advisers are capable of discerning at least some aspects of the managerial decision, what is it they lack? What are they incapable of doing that the politician and corporate manager are so successful in accomplishing? What is this secret ingredient of the great presidents of corporations, universities, and countries that no scientist or ordinary man could ever hope to acquire?

The answer usually given is that the President has information about many different aspects of the world and has an ability to put these aspects together in a way that no analysis could possibly do. In other words, he has a vision of the whole system and can relate the effectiveness of the parts to the effectiveness of the whole. The hidden secret of the great manager, so goes the myth, is his ability to solve the puzzling problems of whole systems that we have been discussing so far.

This answer is a myth, because it is totally unsatisfactory to the reasoning of an intellectually curious person. Are "great" managers fantastically high-speed data processors? Do great managerial minds outstrip any machinery now on the market or contemplated for decades to come? From what we know of the brain and its capabilities, the answer seems to be "no." Indeed, it is doubtful whether the great manager in reaching decisions uses very much of the information he has received from various sources. It is also doubtful whether the manager scans many of the alternatives open to him. In the last chapter we described how the scientist, when he comes to grips with the problems of decision making, discovers that they can only be represented by fairly complicated mathematical models. Even in fairly simple decision-making situations we have come to learn how complicated is the problem of developing a sensible way of using available information. It seems incredible that the so-called successful managers really have inbuilt models that are rich and complicated enough to include the subtleties of large-scale systems.

Suppose for the moment we descend from the lofty heights of the decision makers in Independence Hall and the White House and begin to describe a very mundane and easily recognized managerial problem concerning the number of tellers that should be available to customers in a bank. All of us have experienced the annoyance of going into a bank in a hurry and spending a leisurely but frustrating half hour behind the wrong line. How should the bank manager decide on the allocation of tellers at various times of the day?

This is a fairly simple managerial problem and its like is encountered by thousands of middle managers every day. Furthermore, this problem has been studied quite extensively in operations research and its "solution" is often found in the elementary texts. The texts say that the scientist should try to answer the managerial question by considering both the inconvenience of the customers who wait in the lines and the possible idle time of the tellers who wait at their stations when no customers are there. Thus the "successful" manager can be identified in an objective way, and we need not take a poll of greatness or lack thereof to ascertain whether the manager has performed well. The successful manager will be someone who has properly balanced the two costs of the operation of servicing customers in a bank: the cost of waiting customers and the cost of idle tellers. He will insist that the cost of a minute's waiting of a customer in a line must be compared to a minute's idle time of the teller. On the basis of this comparison, together with suitable evidence concerning the arrival rate of customers and the time required to service each customer, the successful manager will determine the policy concerning allocation of tellers to various stations during the day. Perhaps no one will feel inclined to write the biography of so ordinary a man as the manager of a branch of a local bank, but in any case if this manager decides according to the rational methods just outlined, his biographer may at least be honest about his "greatness."

Nevertheless, the analysis just outlined leaves much unanswered. For example, an idle teller need not be idle while waiting at a station where there are no customers. Instead he may be occupied with other routine matters requiring attention in the administration of the bank. Consequently, if the manager can design the entire operation of his bank's many functions properly, he may be able to decrease the cost of idle time of personnel who are servicing customers. If we look on the other side of the picture, that is, the inconvenience to a customer, we may find that in fact waiting in line is not an inconvenience at all if the customer happens to meet an acquaintance there. Perhaps the manager should serve coffee and doughnuts to waiting customers. Furthermore, if the manager could somehow or other hope to control the behavior of his customers, he might be able to recognize their arrivals in such a way that inconvenience costs are vastly reduced. Add to these considerations other innovations that might be introduced: For example, in many cases banks set up Express Windows to handle customers who would normally have very low service times. Hence, an over-all average waiting time may not make sense if there are different types of service tailored to the various needs of the customers.

But then another, broader consideration occurs to us: Handling the public's financial matters by branch banking methods may be completely wrong. Modern technology may provide ways of developing financial servicing methods far cheaper for both bank and customer. After all, handling cash and checks is an extremely awkward way for a person to acquire goods at a price. With adequately designed information centers, the retail markets need only input information about a customer purchase, and the customer's employers need only input information about his income. Thus every purchase would become simply a matter of centralized information processing, as would a man's weekly or monthly paycheck. There would therefore be no real need for any of us to carry money about and no need to go to a bank and stand patiently in line. But this idea of automated purchasing and income recording is followed by another thought. We realize that any such automated financial system would probably end in eliminating a number of clerical and managerial jobs. Consequently we must examine the social problems of displaced personnel and the need for retraining, otherwise total social costs of automated banking might be far greater than the convenience gained by introducing new technology.

Before we can decide whether the manager of the branch bank is performing "satisfactorily," we must decide a much broader issue—

whether the particular system that the manager operates is an appropriate one. This question leads to deeper considerations concerning the potentials of modern technology and their implications with respect to automation, job training, and the future economics of many lives.

The simple illustration with which we started has now driven us to an almost absurd concept of the "great" manager of even so little a system as a branch bank. The really successful manager must be able to understand the optimal design of the whole bank, as well as the optimal behavior patterns of his customers, and the optimal development of the technology of automation. The great manager of a little enterprise needs to be the great manager of the great enterprise.

This is a curious concept of human behavior that we have been developing. The manager cannot manage well unless he in some sense manages all. Specifically, he must have some idea of what the whole relevant world is like to be able to justify that what he manages is managed correctly.

At the present time we understand very little about managerial behavior, because in all studies of behavior we concentrate our attention on what the observer sees the manager doing; even if we broaden our perspective of his behavior to include the manager's objectives, we usually narrow the scope of these objectives so we are capable of understanding them, that is, of representing them in some kind of analytical form. We have no apparatus in our scientific kit that enables us to observe an activity which must encompass so broad a scope as managerial activity actually implies.

In other words, when we undertake studies to assist mangers, or when we try to understand how managers themselves behave, we are incapable of deciding what the behavior of the manager really means because we are incapable of understanding or observing the manager's whole system. When a system scientist tries to solve a production problem or a government agency problem, he feels there are symptoms of trouble and he wishes to remove them. But he has no means by which he can decide whether the entire activity ought to be redesigned, thereby eliminating both the trouble and the far

more serious loss entailed in a useless set of activities. This is true
whether or not he claims he has used the "systems approach."

We have certainly failed to live up to the lessons that Greek
philosophy tried to teach mankind, namely, that knowledge of oneself is the most important knowledge man can gain. We have undoubtedly done much in biology and psychology to study certain
properties of living organisms and their minds. Our efforts in sociology have been mainly of a descriptive nature, since the sociologist
typically does not try to judge that which he observes, nor even to
understand what the characteristics of an excellent or healthy decision maker might be. Hence there is a serious question whether
what is observed by the "behavioral sciences" is really relevant at
all with respect to the healthy life of the organization. The study
of the health of organizations is thus largely neglected, even though
it is the most important health problem that exists.

The heritage of Western science with its emphasis on observation and logic seems to have provided us with no tools to study managerial activity, even though this is undoubtedly the most important
problem ever faced by man. We simply do not understand the part
of the natural world that is of most concern to us. At best we are
able to say that the good manager is one who has a faith of a proper
sort in what will happen in the world, a faith that he does not attempt to examine or control. Abraham Lincoln, for example, had
the faith that, by trying to preserve the Union through war, an excellent democracy would result. No matter that he failed to understand or have any evidence concerning the implications of the Civil
War in the late decades of the nineteenth and early twentieth centuries. No matter either that Lincoln's whole concept of political
activity might have been wrong. No matter that today we have no
adequate information about what other courses of action were available in the 1860s and what their implications might have been. We
too have a simple faith that Lincoln was a "great" President, or else—
south of the Mason-Dixon line—an equally simple faith that he was
not.

If we are to be honest about our ignorance, we will have to
admit that some managers become great simply because there is

common agreement that they are great. The scientist, the public, and the manager all agree that the decisions made by these great managers were correct, and they agree that there were no other alternatives that would have led to far better results. They also agree that the enterpise in which the manager was engaged was a meaningful one. The scientist might contribute to this agreement by using whatever resources he has available to study the alternatives that were open to the great manager; the public can recognize the benefits they have received from the great manager's activities because they "worked out" well, and the managers themselves through their experience can appreciate what the great manager has accomplished. The public, science, and management come to agree that certain managerial activities are beneficial to the whole system. What results is a judgment of excellence of management based upon such common agreement—not too bad a basis after all in view of the powerful role that common agreement often plays.

We must admit, though, that agreement is a dangerous basis for rational conclusions. Agreement always has its opposite side and often becomes disagreement in the next generation, especially in healthy societies where social change is bound to occur. A rational mind will want to find a far better basis for the judgment of excellence. He will want to find the rational basis in whose terms he can really prove the excellence of managerial decisions, based on an accurate account of the whole system.

Actually, we humans are quite incapable of understanding the agreements we reach. We often take common agreement as expressed in majority opinion to be the end of the matter, even though we frankly recognize that our own judgments are so often inadequate, no matter how strong the agreement behind them.

It may be that as men become politically more astute, they will begin to develop that part of their mentality which enables them to so look at themselves that they can examine the common agreements they hold and adopt a critical attitude toward them. Instead of gaining moral support from the agreements of his fellow man, a person may instead begin to regard agreement as a kind of evidence of danger ahead. He will then be on his way toward what we may call a theory of management, that is, a knowledge about what management really is and not what it is merely perceived to be.

We have been discussing the manager as though he were an object of study of the scientist, and we have been using as an analogy the way in which the scientist observes any kind of living activity. We have seen, however, that science is incapable as yet of generating an adequate science of management simply because it has no basis or technique by which it can adequately judge the difference between good and bad, or healthy and unhealthy, types of managerial behavior. We recognize that there must be such things as a good and a bad manager, but we have no basis on which to decide whether a specific activity falls in one category or the other.

We have also been speaking as though the scientist's interest in management is based mainly on the kind of intellectual curiosity that motivates him to discover the meaning of various mysteries of nature, that is, to transform myth into objectivity.

There is, however, another way in which we should look at the matter: We should realize that science itself is an organized activity, that is, a complex system, and we should examine what the management characteristics of this system are. The typical scientist regards the manager as someone who provides resources and creates the kind of environment in which "high-level" intellectual activity can occur. The scientist has failed to see that the whole problem of management is fundamental to every aspect of his own activities. Rather, he did see this three centuries ago, but saw it in a way that for later science turned out to be unsatisfactory. Thus the idea that management is fundamental to science disappeared in favor of other types of foundations of science. But the scientist is clearly a manager in the broad sense of the term as discussed in this book. If the concept of a great manager is a myth or a mystery, cannot the same be said of the great scientist?

the quality
of science

The scepticism of the last chapter concerning the existence of "great" managers of the past is perhaps not too startling. We all recognize that there are vast differences of opinion as to which of the world's leaders have really attained the stature of greatness, where greatness is meant to imply all the attributes of a farsighted, deep-feeling, wise man. For every praiser of Alexander, Caesar, Napoleon, and Lenin, there is a blamer. It is not too astounding to conclude that we have no objective evidence to judge whether examples of leadership have the quality of being great. Feelings toward greatness must be a matter of personal temperament at best.

On the other hand, when we turn to manifestations of greatness as they occur in science and the arts, it seems clear. enough that we can label a contributor as great and read in the history of science the names that have stood out above the crowd. Why do we feel so secure in our judgment concerning the outstanding quality of scientists and artists, whereas in the case of management no such assurance is forthcoming? It must be that in science there are certain well-recognized foundations, and one can judge whether a contributor to science has built an outstanding structure on these foundations as compared to the structures his contemporaries have built. In other words, science, as opposed to management, seems to contain within itself the criteria that form the basis of the judgment of excellence.

What are these foundations of science that are so clear and so important in making judgments about scientific excellence? The picture that the term *foundation* suggests is a building. The foundations are that upon which the structure rests. Of course this picture is not altogether satisfactory because the entire structure, including its foundations, could not exist did it not also rest upon the earth. The picture in fact suggests that the concept of foundations may be a relative one and raises to the mind the issue of whether or not there are ultimate foundations of science. The classical answer to this question was that there are ultimate foundations beyond which one does not seek to go because the nature of the foundations is so clear.

The two fundamental foundations of science in the classical literature are *logic* and *observation*. The scientist, in other words, builds his entire structure with these two components. Perhaps instead of talking about foundations of a building, one might think of them as the fundamental material out of which the building is constructed. This is no doubt a clearer way to recognize the manner in which logic and observation are fundamental to science, because everything the scientist does consists of exercising logic or making observations, and what he builds is built out of the contributions that logic and observation make available to him.

If we pursue this idea of the foundations of science a little further, we can begin to recognize a clue concerning the concept of the great scientist or his great contributions to science. The great contribution to science is the contribution in which the underlying logical relationships between various descriptions of nature are revealed. Thus, in the great contributions to physical science from the fifteenth to the seventeenth century, there developed a beautifully logical description of the motion of objects not only on the surface of the earth but in the whole universe. One has no difficulty in seeing the immense importance of this logical structure and the manner in which it explains so much of what we observe in the world about us. The persons responsible for the structure are then to be considered great contributors to science, and one can recognize that their contributions have the quality of greatness simply because of what they contribute to our logical understanding of the world.

It might be pointed out, as many have done, that the manner in which the great scientific mind arrives at its conclusions is not necessarily a logical procedure itself. What *is* logical is the structure he builds. The pathway the scientist followed in reaching this structure is usually based on intuition and is always based on unknown processes of his mind which he is either not interested in describing or incapable of describing.

So simple a description of a great contribution to science is of course a vast oversimplification. To delve more deeply into the matter, we need to explore at greater length what constitutes the so-called logical connections between the descriptions of nature.

Specifically, what do we mean when we say that logic is a foundation of science? Clearly what was intended in classical thought was that logic must be a foundation, because above all the scientist must be logically consistent. He must never find himself in the position of asserting on one hand that A is true and on the other hand that A is not true.

So simple a requirement imposed upon the scientist does not seem difficult to meet. Indeed, in ordinary discourse—as we discuss matters with our bosses or our wives—we frequently use this idea of consistency to try to refute the position of another, pointing out that two of the statements used in support of the opponent's position are inconsistent.

Aristotle, in his search for the foundations of all knowledge, proposed his famous law of contradiction, "Nothing can be both A and non-A." This law is in fact a generalization of the idea just introduced. Not only is it correct to say that nothing can be both true and false, but it is also correct to say that nothing can be both yellow and nonyellow, or nothing can be both light and nonlight, and so on. This "law" of science seems unassailable. It is something that all men in fact agree upon, and it is inconceivable that they should do otherwise. To deny the law seems to permit truth and falsity to hold simultaneously and therefore to destroy the whole idea of knowledge or, in general, of human thought.

The *principle of contradiction* is a logical principle, and it seemed to our scientific forefathers of the seventeeth century to be a foundation of science in the truest sense of the term, because it permeates every activity in which the scientist engages. Above all, they said, the descriptions of science must be consistent. If the scientist "violates" this law, then he can be truly accused of becoming nonscientific. The logical criteria of praise and blame are beautifully simple.

And yet, what does the principle of contradiction actually say? That is, what truth of nature does it inform us about?

The investigation of the meaning of the principle of contradiction is both delightful and frustrating. At first sight, and quite obviously, the principle says that no object of nature can have two contradictory properties; thus no one must describe an object in nature to be both heavy and light, or light and dark, or loud and soft, and so on. And yet a little reflection shows us that this cannot possibly be the meaning of the principle of contradiction, simply because objects of nature may be both light and heavy. They may be light at one time, for example, early in their life, and heavy later on, as many an adult male and female well knows. But this is a ridiculous objection to the principle of contradiction. All we need to do is stipulate that implicitly the principle of contradiction means, "Nothing can be both A and non-A *at the same time.*"

But the sceptic so disagreeably questioning the principle of contradiction pushes on, and now he points out that a speaker system, for example, may be loud in one direction and soft in another. Well, says the proponent of the principle of contradiction, we obviously mean, "Nothing can be both A and non-A at the same time and *in the same place.*" The insistent opponent to the principle now goes on to say that the same object at the same time and in the same place may appear light to one observer and dark to another simply because of the localities of the observers or their optical apparatus. The cheerful proponent of the principle now modifies it further. "Nothing can be both A and non-A at the same time and in the same place and *in the same respect.*"

At this point the less enthusiastic pursuers of the meaning of the principle of contradiction will want to quit their pursuit and simply say that the principle of contradiction is true except when it is not true; that is, it is either true or false. The enthusiastic logician will leap in and point out that every statement that anyone can make is either true or false. In fact, he says, this is another principle of logic, and the principle that supposedly forms the foundations of science as well. It is called the *principle of excluded middle* and states that every meaningful statement is either true or false.

But this new principle of excluded middle fares no better than did the principle of contradiction. What does it tell us about the natural world? For example, is it true that everything is either light or dark? Well, certainly not if light and dark are considered to be opposites; some things are moderately shaded. What the proponent of this principle must now claim is that there is a gradation between light and dark and some dividing line. He claims that every object in nature must fall into one of two classes on either side of the dividing line or else on the dividing line itself. What then shall we say of Beethoven's Moonlight Sonata? Is it light or dark? The proponent of the principle must now point out that the principle is only meant to apply to things capable of being either light or dark. Hence the principle reads in its modified form: "Everything is either light or dark that is capable of being either light or dark."

This modification begins to look like another logical principle: "Everything that is *A* is *A*," or in simpler terms, "Everything is identical to itself." However, this is a principle in the history of science that has frequently been denied, at least in the form in which it is intended. All scientific theories and philosophical systems that rest on the concept of change have argued that when one has sufficient knowledge to identify something it thereby loses its identity. Nothing ever remains its identical self for any segment of time.

All this logical nit-picking leads us to the conclusion that if logic is to be thought of as the foundation of science, it must be a foundation in a very peculiar sense. Specifically, it begins to appear that logic tells us nothing about Nature itself, and indeed in the history of logic this has been the conclusion that many logicians themselves have taught their students. Logic, they say, tells us nothing about Nature, but it tells us something about the ways in which we may discuss Nature meaningfully. It is in fact the foundation of the grammar of natural descriptions. And since science consists of describing nature, science must always make use of logic in every one of its descriptions.

But if this is the sense in which logic is a foundation of science, then we can begin to suspect that it is only a relative foundation, just as grammar is a relative foundation of natural languages. We are told that logic provides the underlying rules governing the use of symbols in the language of science. For example, we are told that logic dictates how sentences are to be formed and how inferences are to be drawn between certain sentences. In this sense, however, it is absurd to say that logic does not describe Nature, because surely it describes one of the most natural things in the world—the rules governing the use of language. If the scientist can be regarded as a natural being, then logic describes the way he naturally communicates. One can therefore legitimately ask whether a proposed set of logical rules constitute the optimal way for the users of the language to behave: One may question whether the so-called basic tenets of linguistic usage are proper. This kind of questioning goes on in a very natural way in most ordinary languages as times and events call for changes in the grammar of the language. The same idea, however, applies to the language of science, no matter how formal or artificial it may be. We are not forced to accept one set of rules rather than another, especially when events occurring in the rest of science seem to call for changes or relaxation to certain rules. It begins to look as though "logic" is a component of the whole system, and the "manager" of science needs to look at this component in the same way that any manager examines a component; that is, in terms of the whole system.

And, in fact, managers of all enterprises are concerned with logic in this system sense. For example, one of the problems of great concern to the managers of our military defense system is the construction of a management information system that will permit the managers to be well informed on events of critical importance to them. A management information system does require an underlying logic, that is, a way of displaying material that is most natural to the user. One of the lessons repeatedly learned by persons trying to design management information systems is that they must know a great deal about the whole system of which the manager is a part before they can understand and properly design the logic of the management information system. In other words, the design problem of the logic of a management information system must cope with all the paradoxical problems we have so far discussed in this book. The designer is called upon to look at the whole system to create his design. In this sense it is therefore quite inappropriate to regard the underlying logic of the information system as a "foundation." It is at best a foundation that rests upon the concept of the entire system.

In the last century and a half the scientist has been presented with a number of alternative designs of his management information system. We have inherited from the nineteenth century alternative geometries which enrich the way the scientist can describe the spatial properties of nature. We have also inherited alternative logics, alternative arithmetics, alternative mechanics, and so on. In each of these cases the scientist must choose the manner in which he wishes to present his descriptions of the natural world, that is, he must decide which of the alternative formal languages are most appropriate for his purposes. Might we not guess that the problems of the designer of the language of science are similar to the problems of the designer of the language of management? Might we not say that the choice among alternative modes of describing Nature depends at least in part on considerations of the whole system of science, that is, on the way in which one description of Nature is related to another description of Nature?

If we say these things, we imply that there are no unalterable or irrevocable modes of description, and that principles like the principle of contradiction and the principle of excluded middle simply represent possible choices of the user of scientific language. This does not mean that people will "deny" the principle of contradiction, but rather that they will adapt a certain form of the principle for their own uses. The form that one person may choose can differ from the form someone else will choose in describing another aspect of the natural world.

Of course some principles of science, like conservation of energy, seem to gain—for a while—an almost irrevocable position. But the reason for this can be explained by the way in which the structures of science have been designed and the important role that certain principles—such as the laws of thermal dynamics—play in the structures. Hence so-called foundations become foundations only because changing them in any radical way would necessitate serious remodifications of the rest of the structure, entailing high cost, great inconvenience, great loss of time, and so on. But all managers face exactly the same problem in the formulation of their policies. For an industrial manager to decide to change the location of a plant or drastically to change a product line is a very serious matter, and he is therefore apt to regard his plant location and type of market as a more or less "fixed" foundation of his business: He believes he should not attempt to change the fundamental policy of his firm without considering the high cost and great inconvenience of doing so.

The direction that our reflections have taken in our search for the foundations of science have led us back to the theme of the previous chapter—that the most fundamental aspects of scientific activity rest on certain considerations, there called managerial. Although most scientists would probably object to the word *management* in connection with such matters as the basic logic and mathematics of their discipline, nevertheless the use of the term in the last chapter clearly implies its appropriate use in science. The scientist is a member of a large, complex system, and he has responsibility and authority for making important decisions in the system. There is very little difference in purpose and idea between the manager of an industrial firm who designs the most convenient communication system for members of the firm and the scientist who creates the mathematical language that is most convenient for communication among members of his discipline. Both wish to accomplish in the most convenient and useful form the communication of ideas that are so important in the life of their organization or discipline.

Much the same conclusion is reached if we look at another foundation of science—observation. Observation has always seemed to be a foundation of science to the Western mind because it permits the freeing of the scientist from dogma. If anyone claims that certain characteristics of the natural world are correct, then every one of his peers has the freedom to set up an experiment and observe whether the claim is correct.

In the great centuries of the Renaissance that revolutionized man's search for knowledge, there was a search for principles of human enlightenment of a type that would permit an individual of sufficient intelligence to guarantee to himself that alleged truths about nature were in fact true. Empiricism is a philosophy which declares that man's senses are the origin of all his knowledge. Therefore, if a man is in doubt that nature behaves in a certain way, he has only to test, by means of his own sensory apparatus, whether the asserted description of the natural world holds or does not hold. In the scientific community there is thought to be one ultimate court of appeals: each person's sensory apparatus and its keen ability for making fine distinctions.

Empiricism presents a very beautiful and compelling concept of the foundations of science. It enables the scientist to divorce himself from the overpowering demands of rulers and priests and to free himself as an individual to investigate Nature as She reveals Herself to him. No one can force him to believe anything that his senses tell him is otherwise. The freedom of science consists in our ability to use our senses to test whatever is told to us.

Despite the beauty of this concept of the foundations of science, which in effect is repeated over and over again in the literature about the "meaning of science," great philosophers of the past have frequently presented a basic doubt about such foundations, a doubt that reason, when pursued to its ultimate, cannot adequately remove. It was the rational doubt expressed in Descartes' *Meditations*. The doubt recurred in many writings of philosophers of the seventeenth and eighteenth centuries. These philosophers subscribed to a philosophy called *rationalism* in which reason and especially logic were regarded to be the foundations of science. The rational doubt about empiricism is based on the very simple idea that the senses could tell us false things. What is the basis on which we believe that which our senses tell us? One analogy of the sense apparatus of a human is the input device of a computer. But we all know that a computer can accept falsity as readily as it accepts truth. If our senses tell us that this is light and not dark, how are we to know whether the input from nature is not a complete falsity?

Unfortunately, whenever the empiricist seriously considers this challenge to his foundations, he usually enters into rather murky waters. He tries to claim that there are certain "simple" sensations which are so forcefully impressed upon the mind that there can be no doubt about the veracity of the sensation. And indeed, if doubts do occur, it is possible to appeal to other minds to gain agreement.

This is a very curious and alarming answer to the rationalist doubt. It means that the empirical foundations are not foundations at all. Instead, some kind of "feeling of the forcefulness of the sensation" plus "agreement" becomes the foundation. But to make these the foundations of science is absurd. We all know that a group of people can stand in a field observing objects flying in the sky above, that all can agree on the "forcefulness of their sensations," and by a kind of mass hysteria come to rather detailed but completely false descriptions of the flying objects about which they all agree strongly. No, it cannot be the forcefulness of the sensation plus agreement that constitutes the foundation of observational truth. It must be that, in addition, the scientist introduces very careful *control* procedures so that when sensation and agreement occur, the control procedures assure him that what is being observed is correct.

Indeed, the whole idea of a forceful sensation is completely irrelevant so far as the validity of sensation is concerned. A computer, for example, might recognize differences between the forcefulness of various kinds of inputs in terms of the force used on the keyboard of a typewriter. But if the computer had such an inbuilt capability, this would certainly not provide it with any guarantee that the forceful inputs were more accurate than the less forceful ones; strong people are not necessarily right people.

To save his foundations, the empiricist is forced to say that science is concerned with "carefully controlled observations" and the agreements reached about observations are reached only in the context of careful control. The ideas of simple sensation and direct observation by themselves have nothing whatsoever to do with the observational foundation of science. These concepts only become relevant in the context of controlled experimentation and measurement.

What does control of observation mean? It means that the scientist is capable of judging whether or not extraneous causes have influenced the observations; it means that he can judge the extent to which the observation has been influenced by unforeseen or unknown events.

Again our reflections have forced us back into an analogy with problems of all managers. Managerial control is a fundamental concept of management. The manager must know that the operations of his organization are "in control," and he must be sure to exert various kinds of control procedures. In some of the more interesting cases these control procedures consist in "managing by exception," where the manager intervenes only when signals are sent back that there is lack of control in one or more parts of the organization. Anyone who has had experience in managing recognizes the difficulties of setting up an adequate managerial control system, and also recognizes that the basis of designing such a system depends on some perspective of the entire system. For example, there are very petty controls occurring in many organizations whenever procedures are introduced to control insignificant expenditures. These petty control procedures require many members of the organization to spend intolerably boring hours counting pennies and reporting the results of their counts. Poor managerial control of this kind stems from an inability of certain members of the organization to understand in what sense control procedures are important, that is, from a failure to understand the characteristics of the whole system.

Much the same could be said about control in science itself. The young scientist is often trained to exert very careful control in his experimentation so that when he reports his results in scientific journals he cannot be accused of failing to take into account variables that might have influenced the outcome. On the other hand, much control in science turns out to be extremely petty. The scientist chooses to study those aspects of nature where he recognizes that he can control the variables, but the studies themselves turn out to be of the most trivial and insignificant sort. The literature of science becomes filled with reports of experiments that were "very carefully done" but were of very little or no importance to man in his pursuit of knowledge of the natural world.

Thus science, like management, faces the problem of designing control procedures that will most effectively gain its objectives. It is by no means easy to see how these procedures are to be designed; exactly the same perplexing problems occur in the case of the definition of control in science as occur in the definition of control in management.

We see then that neither logic nor observation can be considered as "ultimate" foundations of science. The meaning of both logic and observation depend on difficult and often unsolved problems of the management of science.

Now rationalism of the seventeenth century suggested a much more fundamental question concerning the foundations of science than empiricism was ever willing to do. Even if it is true that contemporary scientists by means of observation and logic have succeeded in answering some of the puzzling questions about Nature, few would dare assert that the enterprise will soon be over and that most of the properties of Nature will have been discovered in the next decades. Rather, the enlightened scientist well knows that the results appearing so powerful and convincing today may be overthrown tomorrow. He knows that new aspects of the natural world may be discovered that are not being even remotely investigated today. In this regard, Kant's marvelous conclusion to one of his books is appropriate: "Two things fill my heart with never ending awe: the starry heavens above and the moral law within." Two things that man in mid-twentieth century knows very little about are the properties of life and matter in space and the properties of his own moral law that govern his political behavior. In other words, he knows very little about the starry heavens or about himself. Yet both pursuits of science seem perfectly reasonable, and the more optimistic among us hope that the next generations will not only have the opportunity of exploring the moon, Mars, and the more distant spatial bodies, but also that international man will grow up, become an adult living being, and begin to know a great deal more about himself, his needs, the reasons for his conflicts, and the pathways by which a more mature life may occur even on earth.

Reason, in its insistence on understanding, poses a more fundamental question to the scientific mind than questions concerned with observation and logic. It poses the question of what guarantees the survival of the scientific enterprise. If truth is always one large step beyond where we are, what guarantees that we can take even the smallest step in this direction?

It was a question such as this that led the rationalists of the sixteenth and seventeeth centuries to argue that managerial control, so important to science, presupposes the existence of a God who acts as a guarantor of the survival of science and the reliability of science's results.

No doubt it will seem strange to a mind trained in the sciences of today to suggest that theology might be a foundation of science, but just such a suggestion was made three centuries ago by the rationalists, and no one has convincingly shown why this suggestion is inappropriate. The feeling of devotion to a deity is not the hallmark of the rationalist religion; rather the rationalist's God is an essential part of any attempt to understand the world. The reason for this is very simple. God is that particular part of Nature that guarantees the validity of man's beliefs, or, in more general terms, guarantees men's ability to pursue truth. What particular thing is it about the natural world that assures us that our search for truth will be successful? If our answer to this question is that nothing in the natural world provides such a guarantee, then this is also a theological principle, and the reflective mind has every reason to investigate why such a skeptical principle has validity. Theology is concerned with the study of the properties of God, and the question whether something with these properties can be assumed to exist. Finally, theology investigates whether such an existent thing provides the kind of guarantee required by those who seek knowledge or those who manage in order to be assured of their controls.

THE QUALITY OF SCIENCE 43

Today we can no longer believe in the "proofs" of God's existence that were developed by rationalist philosophers. Too many
questions about the natural world and the nature of logical proof
have been raised to enable us to say that God's existence follows
from a fairly simple pattern of reasoning. Nonetheless, the political
events of the last decade and the strong interrelationship between
science and the political world must bring the scientific mind back
to the classical question of its own survival and control. And as the
scientific mind begins to raise this question again to consciousness,
it may very well be that theology will take on the role it had in the
consideration of the foundations of science in the seventeenth century. This is a theme that needs to be explored more fully in later
parts of this book.

However we pursue the problems of the foundation of science,
either by the pathway of logic or observation or of the guarantor,
we inevitably reach the same conclusion—that the foundations of
science can be construed as a type of management. The considerations concerning the survival of the activity of science led us to conclude that its foundations may rest in a type of theology, but the
theology that we have been considering also falls within the scope
of management in its broadest sense. For management is the activity
of selecting from among alternatives in the pursuit of goals and especially the goals of large-scale organizations of which science is
clearly one. The principles that guarantee the survival of science
will therefore be managerial principles. The foundations of science,
in other words, lie in its management philosophy. The great scientists of the past can be construed as great managers of the scientific
enterprise, however different they may appear to us from current-day
managers. These scientists are considered great because the decisions
they made seem to have helped produce the enormous gains of
science as it is recognized today.

But the lessons we learned from the last chapter are applicable
here as well. Perhaps the pathways selected by great scientists of
the past are not the most adequate ones for science to have pursued.
There can be no question that science, elegant as it may be today,
has ignored some of the most fundamental problems of the human

race—specifically, its biology, psychology, and social life. Perhaps this very unfortunate situation arose because of the choices of the so-called great minds of the past. In any event, we have no way of knowing whether the so-called great scientists of the past might not have selected far better uses for their scarce resources than they actually did.

One might respond to these remarks by pointing out that brilliant minds are clearly recognizable within the context of their own work, and it is not necessary to view the whole system of science or society to judge whether a great contribution has occurred. It is typical of the scientific community to regard brilliance of mind as a characteristic of greatness, because brilliance can be recognized directly by the way the scientist behaves and what he produces. Thus insight and so-called creativity are supposed to be the hallmarks of all one might wish for in the great scientist. But this attitude toward excellence is itself a management philosophy, a philosophy of personnel evaluation; as a philosophy it entails some very serious weaknesses. It is questionable whether any so-called brilliant minds constitute greatness in a defensible sense of the term, because if their brilliance is applied in the wrong direction or in narrow ways, the end results may be far more destructive than they are productive. Ascribing greatness to people is a part of the general managerial function of evaluating performance, a function that is not well understood despite considerable writings on the topic.

What can be said then about management that makes any sense either in science or to any other aspect of the large-scale systems we humans inhabit? Are philosophies of management purely individual? Are we to conclude that one cannot make comparisons of better and worse, and that "improvement" is a meaningless term when applied to large-scale systems? Are we to conclude that there is no basic foundation for the creation of a more satisfactory world? Must we say, for example, that the management philosophy of fascism is as good as the management philosophy of democracy or of communism or of anarchism? Must we say that "it all depends on who the individual is," who his friends are, and how they feel about each other? Must we conclude that no comparison of good and bad in connection with the fundamental philosophy of management can ever occur? That the ethics of whole systems are meaningless?

Of course we can say all these things, and they have been said repeatedly, but why should we? It is surely impolite to our forebears who fought so hard for progress and human improvement to throw away all that they strove so hard to attain. Indeed, those who take a pessimistic attitude toward life often do so in the most lazy or puerile fashion. They believe it only necessary to point out the dangers that men face and use most superficial evidence concerning man's ultimate fate. Living men believe they become better at doing certain things. Living men believe they have learned from their experience as well as the experience of the human race. Living men believe there is such a thing as civilization and civilized living, and that this is a better form of life than noncivilized living. Living men believe the human spirit can attain higher forms of life by means of its own efforts as well as by means of biological breeding.

What is it that characterizes man's progress? What is it that differentiates between good and bad in the policies of whole systems?

the idea
of progress

Basic to any idea of system improvement and the development of a philosophy of management of large-scale systems is the concept of progress. Although use of the term *progress* by both sides of the international political battle of today has somewhat jaded the term in the eyes of the ordinary man, nevertheless it retains its original importance for the development of a philosophy of life in human systems.

To think about progress is to regard the past in order to speculate about the future in an evaluative mood. We have already said some things about the concept of improvement of society, but progress is an even richer idea. Improvement means a change for the better compared to the past state of affairs. Progress means not only a present change for the better but betterment in the future as well. When we speak of progress, we speak of what the world will be like as much as what it has been like. To believe in progress is to believe that this world today is a step, or a phase, of a whole series of steps. The helpful analogy is a mathematical series, like $\frac{1}{2}$, $\frac{3}{4}$, $\frac{7}{8}$, $\frac{15}{16}$, ... ; each number is greater than its predecessor, and at each stage of the series greater things are to follow. This number series has a "limit," the number 1, which will never be reached by the series but will be approximated more and more closely. In the same way, in the concept of progress there is some "ideal" state, usually not attainable, but with succeeding generations the ideal can be approximated more and more closely.

In the first chapter we considered mere improvement and asked ourselves how we know that we have changed for the better over a prior state of affairs. Now we ask how we can assure ourselves that we progress as well, that is, that the next and subsequent steps will approximate an ideal.

In a way it may seem too bold to turn to a consideration of progress after discovering the difficulty of finding evidence for mere improvement. If we have no evidence for mere improvement, how can we expect to find evidence for progress? Yet there is something to be said for making our difficult problems more general rather than more specific, because in generalizing we can sense the real meaning of the underlying difficulty. We said in the past three chapters that evidence of social improvement demands a view of the whole system; the concept of progress is one way of looking at the whole system in terms of steps toward an ideal.

Progress is both an attractive and persuasive idea. We like to believe that the human species, despite its ups and downs, is marching on toward an ever more ideal state of living.

The theory of evolution supports this belief in the progress of man. Evolution has convinced us that the various living species can be put into some sort of hierarchy, and we can talk about lower and higher forms of life. Aristotle did very much the same thing when he tried to show how each higher form of life adds some function to the functions performed by the lower forms. When one comes to man, according to Aristotle, one finds the most fully developed expression of the living organism in which all the living functions can be displayed, and the highest one—the ability to "contemplate"—belongs only to man. Aristotle goes on to depict the "ideal" life of contemplative man. In the theory of evolution much has been said about the ability of the living organism to adapt to its environment, and here again man seems to sit at the pinnacle of the development of the species. We can begin to picture an ideal biological species with supreme capability of adaptation.

It is natural for us to think that within the history of our own species we find an evolutionary development, because man has the special ability of inheriting from the past the gains made in "conquering Nature." Consequently man "evolves" not only through biological determinism but also through his own conscious effort. Each age can say that it is building upon the accomplishments of the previous age and hence is an improvement over the previous era, and that this process or progress will never stop.

In these days one of our favorite ways of defending our belief in progress is to compare the state of technology of past generations with the state of technology today.

We like to point out that a century ago the only way a man could successfully travel from one city to another was to walk or use a walking animal. The rate of travel at 10 miles an hour would have been considered impossible if carried on over a long period of time. Now it is commonplace to travel across the surface of the world for long periods at the rate of 10 miles per minute. The supersonic transport will increase this to 30 miles per minute. The ideal is some virtual "zero time" to cover the mile.

Two generations ago the only way one person could communicate with another some distance away would be to either walk to him or send a written communication by means of a walking animal. Today it is commonplace to simply pick up a telephone and within a minute or so speak to a distant friend. In another generation, communication will be accomplished in a second's flip of a switch.

Perhaps even more fascinating evidence of technological progress is the development of more successful ways of taking care of the human body. A decade ago people with certain heart ailments were doomed; today, with the development of heart operations, they can survive for many years. The most popular measure of technological progress in the area of health is the increase in the average life of the human being which for certain populations has tripled in the past few centuries. In the next generation the average life span may be eighty. The ideal is immortality on earth.

We have already mentioned that practically every adult of a civilized country has the opportunity to receive an education that would have been available only to the very wealthy or a privileged few of previous generations. The next generation will educate all people of all nations. The ideal is a perfect education tailored to the specific needs of each person on earth.

Today we are capable in some countries of nourishing those who for various physical and economic reasons are not able to find resources for the sustenance of their life. Our abundance of food is like a huge cornucopia compared to the supply of food in generations past. The next generation will adequately feed the world. The ideal is a perfect meal, whenever required, tailored to the specific tastes of each person on earth.

All these and similar speculations about technological progress, including our ability to soar farther and farther into space, paint images of time to come. The popular mythology of our current age is science fiction, which, instead of portraying the adventures of gods and heroes of the past, tells us stories about heroes of the future world who in the environment of an immensely expanded technology will be able to do far greater things than we could possibly imagine in this age. Science fiction mythology blots out the pessimism of those who declare the impossibility of speed in excess of the velocity of light, or the cure of certain bodily ailments on the basis of what we now know. Realizing that innovation is a central part of technological progress, we come to accept as common sense the idea that most problems of a technological sort are eventually susceptible to solution, and that there are no limits to the improvement of men.

Finally, we must recognize how much more science knows of the natural world today than it knew even a few decades ago. Physics of the 1920s must be regarded as naïve groping compared to the sophisticated physics of today. Biology has opened new vistas concerning the nature of life. Even the social sciences have come to learn a great deal about the human being and his interrelationships with other men. The next generation will "break through" the barriers of our knowledge of the mind and society. The ideal is that every man in his way will attain the knowledge he needs to accomplish what he wants.

We could continue in this vein, talking about technological

progress and beginning to sense a feeling of optimism concerning the inevitable improvements of the human system, were it not for the reflections that have always countered these feelings of optimism. We have already expressed the idea in these pages that for every so-called technological improvement, there is all too obvious to us the opposite—a technological degradation.

Most outstanding of the degradations of technology is war. We now have a capability of conducting war in a far "better" way than did any of our predecessors. Whereas a single soldier could effectively kill only one enemy with a single arrow or a single knife in ages gone by, one man can now accomplish the killing of thousands simply by pushing a button. In the next generation it may be a whole nation. The "ideal" military technology is the annihilation of the human race in an instant.

But if we try to look at the positive side of our military accomplishments, we attempt to assure ourselves that the technological discoveries of various modern weapons provide man with a defense against the evil intents that often lurk in the corners of the human race, for example, the intent to conquer and put into slavery. We are far better able to defend ourselves than were our predecessors. The ideal is a perfect defense against crime and international gangsterism. But a moment's reflection shows that this is like praising ourselves for having developed an insecticide to take care of a mosquito that had only developed by our own inept use of previous insecticides. It's the counterpart of DeMorgan's philosopher in *Budget of Paradoxes* who was so thankful that God had discovered centripetal forces to counteract centrifugal forces; as DeMorgan points out, He might better have left both forces out of His design. Man has created the need for defense by creating the very weapons that make defense possible.

No, it is impossible in any way to regard the developments of the various weapons and counterweapons of the current military age as constituting technological progress. Their development is symptomatic of a kind of degradation of the social order with which man has not yet been able to cope.

This degradation is manifest in our inability to negotiate the political problems we face. We simply have no technology of any adequate sort that can guarantee peaceful discussion of issues when a world crisis or national crisis or local crisis occurs. Instead, we must always face the reality that negotiations will break down and deadly conflict result.

In terms of the concept of progress, the antitechnologist believes we are *less* able to negotiate favorably than were our predecessors, and in the complex world of tomorrow negotiation will be even more difficult. The "ideal" we are rushing toward, he says, is international chaos where no one understands anyone else.

The antitechnologist goes on to describe how, at the individual level, we have no way of creating a society in which individual protest is possible against social policies. All we do is to implement the technology of "law and order" and use it against those who feel very strongly that certain political policies, like the buildup of weapons, are evil. Those in control of national policies must often take the protesters, no matter how many in number nor how rational their position, and put them into jail or fine them, much as though they were the same sort of individual as the criminal.

The degradation resulting from man's inability to handle negotiation and protest and man's enormous development of the instruments of war are examples of the technological "progress" that has been brought about along with our great technological successes. For each technological "success" the antitechnologist can readily find a corresponding technological degradation. In the case of travel we have only to note that the ability to travel at high speeds more or less at the will of the individual results in an enormous number of deaths, as well as in the social evils of smog, noise, and the ugliness of much of our transportation system.

Nor can we deny that the freedom to communicate has also introduced an enormous change in the social life of the individual. Each of us must now comply with the request to communicate whether we want to or not, for example, by responding to the telephone at its every ring. Real privacy cannot be attained in modern technological societies; to attain it one must go off to some "underdeveloped" country.

Nor can we make claims for success in the area of health until we have shown that an individual whose body is maintained in a healthy state is pursuing a way of life that for him is meaningful. We have found no technological way of coping with boredom and other forms of the degradation of mental health. Perhaps man is better off if he dies young, considering our complete failure to understand the life problems of a "normal" forty-year-old. Consider, too, the danger of extrapolating success in medicine to the next generation, when so many "gains" in stamping out disease themselves introduce multiple problems of immunity in the subsequent life of the species.

In the field of education, it is easy enough to describe the degradation that has occurred as mass education has become the theme of the day. Less and less thought is put into the individual differences occurring among the young or among adults. Instead, the technology of education forces the same kind of curriculum on everybody—even at the level of the most superior students who are trying to gain their doctoral degrees. The most ridiculous kind of defense is put up for the standardization of the educational system. We try to claim that "general education" is required and that the student should "cover many different areas" so that he will not become "too narrow." All these clichés, however, become translated into a deadly series of standardized courses with the most uninspiring texts, in an environment where the teacher, no matter what his original motivation, must quickly accede to the boredom of the affair and the students follow suit. The "ideal" of this sort of technological progress seems to be precision: precisely the same input for all regardless of their individuality.

Finally, in the area of social welfare, it is easy enough to argue that many of our policies simply attack the dignity of the human being by forcing him to comply with many kinds of regulations in order to attain support from society. If he claims support he is always subject to investigation, because, according to those in power, many people try to claim support who do not deserve it. Compliance with the regulations forced by the state makes the recipient of social welfare virtually admit that he is a less-than-adequate member of society. The "ideal" of social welfare seems to be control: Every individual seeking aid will be maximally scrutinized.

There are several models of technological progress. First, technology can be conceived of as a kind of progress or a kind of degradation. If we concentrate attention on one aspect of society, as many people have, then it is possible to show that in some sense the present age is an improvement over the past age, and that there are ideals that the next generation will still more closely approach. But if we wish to turn pessimistic, it is easy enough to look at technological gains from a point of view in which they become technological degradation—inabilities rather than abilities to cope with the problems of society—and will become worse in the next generation. A third model of technology says that technology is "neutral" with respect to progress, that technological changes have very little to do with the ethics of whole systems.

Proponents of the degradation theory of technology will say that in those societies where technology has been raised to the highest level, as in fascism, it is easy enough to recognize the social degradation from a civilized point of view. These societies often base their propaganda on the idea of "increased efficiency of operation." They have almost always displayed a strongly evil side as well as a progressive side. Fascism is famous for its ability to build highways, make trains run on time, improve the postal system, telephone system, and so on. In Germany during the 1930s the social state displayed great efficiency in reducing unemployment; every able-bodied member of society was assured of gaining an income sufficient to meet his needs and those of his family. But we hardly need to be reminded of the costs the total society had to pay to maintain this kind of "social efficiency" and the outrageous propaganda required to persuade members of the society that "progress" had indeed occurred; even the concentration camps and gas chambers were run efficiently.

The theory of technological progress admits that every step forward involves dangerous side effects that must be avoided by planning, or quickly recognized if the plan fails in some regard. Thus the model claims that if we try hard, keep flexible, and develop keen adaptive techniques, we shall progress.

The theory of technological neutrality says that no technological change by itself—no matter how attractive or threatening it may appear to the individual—has any positive or negative value unless it is considered in relation to the general system.

But instead of examining the meaning and validity of these models, we should ask ourselves what kind of structure a society should have. What constitutes a healthy state of society? What criteria can we look for that will indicate positive value in the social order?

We are all well aware of the fundamental debate going on in the world at present concerning the question of social values. On the one hand in the West there is a strong emphasis on the value of freedom of the individual to make his own choices, for example, the choice of the people who will govern, the choice of his career, the choice of his wife, the choice of his own way of living. In the Eastern sector of the world, however, there is a strong objection to the negative value of exploitation, that is, the negative value of the economic advantage that certain individuals have over other individuals.

The positive value of freedom has long been recognized in historical writings. Men have extolled the idea of individual freedom ever since the earliest days of Greek philosophy. But men have also pointed out the need for a well-organized society based on rational, nonexploitative principles, also since the days of Greek philosophy.

The value of individualism seems opposed to the value of social planning. The basic notion of individualism is that if individuals are given freedom of choice, by their own initiative they will create a social order far better than one could design by setting down rational principles and then forcing them upon the members of society.

Opposed to the value of individualism is the value of "rationality" in social planning. The rational planner recognizes that if one does permit freedom then men typically resort to actions in which they attempt to exploit their fellow men. Exploitation means the act of enforcing certain social policies that are of benefit to oneself but are counter to the values of one's fellow men. If we carefully examine life in the industrial systems of Western nations today, there can be no question that the vast majority of people spend most of their time in activities they would prefer not to engage in. Indeed, they regard their weekends and vacations as escapes from the hours of work which from their point of view are either boring or at least far from satisfying. There are, however, a few people, the managers and owners, who benefit considerably from the activities of the industrial society and who would not change their activities even if given the opportunity of doing so. A happy executive would rather be at his desk than not, but the worker in the plant would certainly rather not be in the plant and would rather be undertaking some other activity more appealing to his nature.

Although one side claims that freedom to vote forms the basis of value in the social order, and the other side claims that freedom from exploitation forms the basis, in the actual implementation of social policy both sides obliterate the very values they extol. In the Western world it is foolish to claim that every individual has the free choice of voting for government officials or of selecting his career or his mode of living. The selection of government officials is largely dictated by political caucuses, and the average individual is only given a sort of second-level choice once the basic policy has been decided. In the East, many individuals live lives they would prefer not to live, while a select number of individuals of the bureaucracy and "higher" levels of science enjoy a life that is essentially most pleasing to them. Whatever one may wish to say in political propaganda, freedom of individual expression does not exist in the world today any more than lack of exploitation does.

The moral of all these reflections is the same one we have discussed throughout this book, namely, that if one concentrates on one sector of a system, it may indeed be possible to find signs of progress or improvement and even to develop a satisfactory theory of ethics regarding the sector. However, as soon as the sector is put in relation to the whole system, then all the criteria that seemed so satisfactory before turn out to appear the opposite. The ethics of the large-scale system is usually at variance with the ethics of a sector.

But these reflections about values need not discourage us. It may be true that no large-scale system that man could possibly devise at the present time is a perfect one. Nevertheless, it may be possible to find basic root values out of which all other values stem, that is, certain basic measures of the total performance of the system that enable us to judge whether *total* system improvement has occurred. Thus, freedom of choice and freedom from exploitation are two facets of the basic value of total social welfare. For example, we might be able to study two nations, East and West, and even though we could point out obvious deficiencies in both cases, we might nonetheless be able to decide that one nation was "better run" than the other, because when one calculates the total benefits and costs of each, the one nation comes out much higher along the scale.

What kind of basic value criterion should we use? In the search for criteria of system progress and the gauging of the quality of a social system, scientists have typically followed one of two avenues, the first based upon the biological analogy of the evolution of the living being and the second upon the more direct approach of finding such measures as the satisfaction or utility of a social system for its members.

The biological analogy states that the known evolution of living beings on the earth provides us with clues concerning the evolution of social forms, and hence it is possible to measure the level of life of the social organism just as it is possible to gauge the level of development of a given living organism. In the history of thought the biological analogy has appeared in many different forms. Recall that, according to Aristotle, the highest living form is man, who has the ability to contemplate, and therefore by analogy the highest social form will be a society that permits maximum opportunity for each individual man to exercise his highest function. According to the Aristotelian theory, the most highly developed or ideal societies are those in which there is maximum opportunity for man to express what characterizes him as a man.

As the centuries went by, the biological analogy was expressed in many other ways, particularly in the notions of self-fulfillment. Instead of finding one common characteristic that all people share, for example, ability to think, one also looks at all those characteristics which peculiarly belong to a given individual, his art, his love, as well as his knowledge; the society that permits the fullest expression of the individual life is the richest society. Very seldom has any attempt been made to measure the development of a society in terms of self-fulfillment, but the basic idea of this as a criterion of progress has frequently been discussed in the history of thought.

In more recent times, the biological theme of progress has been captured in the discussions of cybernetics and adaptive systems. Cybernetics is the discipline concerned with the way in which individuals pursue—or ought to pursue—their goals. It emphasizes the importance of equilibrium, of an internal state that is capable of responding to environmental change without the system's getting off its chosen course. If one objects that this kind of adaptation to the environment is only a part of the story, because the goal itself may be evil, the cybernetician will reply that the only legitimate meaning of an evil goal is one whose pursuit inevitably leads to disaster—that is, to disequilibrium. Thus a ship ought not to sail toward the rocky shore, because if it does it will fly apart. Perhaps it ought not to be on this journey at all, because the journey will take it into the habitat of pirates. Perhaps it ought not to be a ship of this design, because over time it will deteriorate too rapidly. But there may be some voyage and some ship for mankind where the guarantees of equilibrium are built-in, so to speak. Such a design of craft and voyage represents the ideal of cybernetic progress.

Many will feel some uneasiness about this approach to progress; it seems to say that the good is merely survival and that evil is disaster, without telling us why we should survive, or why "falling apart" isn't a good idea. Instead of determining how to keep the human machine operating smoothly, perhaps we should determine what it is that men basically wish to do in their lives. We should try to develop a social structure in which people are given maximum opportunity to satisfy their basic needs as well as gain any other goals they wish to acquire. The proper term might be one of power; that is, the social structure should supply sufficient power to every member of its society so that each member can acquire what he wishes and certainly what he needs.

In the case of a single individual this measure of his development seems on intuitive grounds to work out rather satisfactorily. One determines the goals the individual wishes most to attain, then one tries to develop what is called a utility function appropriate to a single individual. This utility function measures the relative importance of various kinds of goals in the near and distant future. As previously pointed out, this was the basic idea behind Jeremy Bentham's pleasure-pain calculus, which was suggested to him by the writings of David Hume. But despite the attractiveness of utility maximization as an idea, the difficulties of obtaining an adequate measure of the utilities of a single individual are obvious, especially when one considers his private life. How should one compare the "utility" of different kinds of friendship or different kinds of love affairs? Is the affection of a man's wife more important to him than the deep friendship he may hold for a colleague, and how should one gauge the safety of a man's children compared, let's say, to the utility of his automobile or of his business? Because these questions are so hard to answer, the utility approach to the study of system development has concentrated most on the areas where the utilities can be successfully measured in terms of financial profit.

The attempt, however, to apply utility theory to the public domain, that is, to the ethics of whole systems, has been far from successful. There are the difficulties of comparing the utilities of two or more individuals, which in principle is always possible but hard to implement. There are also the difficulties of incorporating the many different kinds of goals that individuals wish to attain. Anyone who has spent time on the problems of urban planning and development well knows the multitude of different interests that are represented in the urban community and the difficulties of implementing any kind of so-called rational plan. Consider, for example, the vexing problem of water resources in areas where water is scarce. Each community believes that it has a certain kind of priority because of either the location of the water supply or the size of the community. Each will look upon the water resource in terms of its own individual needs and the planner will find it practically impossible to develop any universally acceptable criteria for the allocation of the resource. Each interest tries to override proposed plans simply because they look detrimental to the particular community.

Nonetheless, there is the basic idea that somehow or other, with more understanding about the nature of the human being and his wants, one can begin to arrive at measures of social development that serve the total utility or satisfaction of the inhabitants of the system. Of course one test of the accuracy of such a measure is whether the different interests in the public domain will accept a plan developed according to the utility measure. If they do not, then in some sense the planners have failed to measure the social utility relative to a given system of human beings. It would be foolish of the planners to claim that the inhabitants of the system are simply ignorant if they fail to adopt the plan; the planners must recognize that one test of their measurements is the acceptance by the system of the suggested plan. Even though the planners may not be successful at the outset, however, they may believe that through education and further research men of good will and sufficient reason will begin to understand each other, to see that the concessions that may be necessary to serve the interests of someone else are not in fact a backing down on the part of the courageous man but rather an expression of social courage. The more optimistic among the planners will hope to incorporate into a vastly expanded utility concept all the wishes, needs, and requirements of a society, as well as the unexpressed but nevertheless very important requirements of the generations to come. Indeed, we could not be so selfish and inbred as to ignore the fact that many of our policies may be detrimental to another generation no matter how pleasing to ours. A rationalist in his approach to the development of social utilities must incorporate what he estimates to be the requirements of the world's future inhabitants.

Of course so vast a program of research into society is well beyond either our present inclinations or our capabilities. We are far more inclined to put whatever research talents we have into the much more mundane and obviously safe kinds of research that deal with special problems of specific sectors of society in today's environment. We haven't even undertaken to do the rather obvious if superficial census of man's needs and wants and resources around the world.

Our experts tell us that the only feasible way to plan for progress is piecemeal planning. What they fail to tell us is that their own prescription is based on a postulate of planning, namely, that if we improve sector by sector, leaving out considerations of the whole world, or of the whole nation, or of generations to come, our improvements will add up to social progress. The postulate on the face of it appears foolish, and there is certainly no evidence of its truth.

It is a mistake to use man's failure to develop an adequate measure of the utility of the social structure as evidence that such attempts are futile. There is every reason to urge that we vastly enlarge our study of man and his requirements far beyond the present very inadequate status of this research. We need to pursue as far as we can the possibility that there is an underlying value of a social structure which can provide the basis for a theory of progress, that is, the ethics of large-scale systems.

Nevertheless, since the theme of our discussion is in the philosophical mode, we should introduce some cautions as well as counterarguments that may occur to the reflective and rational mind.

First of all, each of us has, in the secret part of his life, a strong sense and inclination toward evil as well as good. It is very nice to say that men should live cooperatively and destroy their weapons and cease violent warfare. But there is obviously a basic need on the part of many people to express themselves in the mode of conflict, and they so express themselves quite readily when the opportunity arises. There is also in each of us a bit of the trickster, so that even in the most peaceful and serene situations, suddenly there comes upon us the inclination to destroy what appears so beautiful. It is probably quite natural for those who wander among the beauties of a glass shop in Venice to have the silly urge to sweep their arm across a shelf of fragile pieces, or to suddenly want to tramp through a beautiful garden of tulips, or pull a chair out from under some dignified individual, or cut the throat of a very devoted friend. The distance between mischief and outright evil is often very small.

If we say, therefore, that we are to gauge the development of a society by the degree of its ability to satisfy the wants of individuals, what are we to say about these negative wants, the expression of mischief and evil that is a natural part of each one of us?

Well, we might say that we should also incorporate into any scheme of social values the theories and ideas about the equilibrium of living forms which have been generated within cybernetics and other disciplines. We would then say that the transformation from mischief to evil constitutes a biological breakdown, and therefore it is necessary for society to take whatever steps are appropriate to prevent such biological degeneration. We would go on to say that the aim of a society is to provide the greatest utility for the greatest number, subject, however, to certain equilibrium constraints that prevent the expression of people's wishes in the form of evil. Perhaps this could be done by some kind of basic psychoanalysis or biological analysis of each individual which would then become part of his upbringing and maturation. The result might bring about the kind of guarantees for future generations that were mentioned above.

In effect we would be saying that the utility function of a total society must be measured in terms of the "legitimate" goals of the individuals in society. Legitimacy is to be measured by the extent to which the accomplishment of the goal does not interfere in a negative way with welfare of other members of the society. In saying that the "greatest good of the greatest number" must be served, we mean that we must sift out of the mixtures of lives those illegitimate goals that make others—of the present or future—unhappy.

There is a still deeper reflection that makes us hesitate to use utility or satisfaction alone as the basis of progress. It is a reflection based on the very obvious idea that man, once he has attained his goals, whatever they may be, often finds their attainment the least satisfactory thing of all. The utopians of the nineteenth century actually hoped to find a society that would supply to every man what he really required for his life. What they often failed to realize was that once man is supplied in such a manner, he may well find that life is no longer worth living, or at least has become far from "satisfactory" for him.

We must indeed question the basic axiom of economics and

other forms of normative ethics arising from the notions of utility maximization and satisfaction. The axiom that every man seeks to maximize his own good may simply be false. What would falsify it? Why the thought that what each man most desires, or at least desires strongly, is the ability to struggle for something that he has not attained, that each man finds the meaning of life in its tragedy as well as its comedy, in despair as well as joy, in struggle as well as attainment. This is certainly not a new idea. It has been expressed so frequently in literature and philosophy as to make one seem foolish to ignore it. For example, those who propose that heaven consists of an environment in which each man finally enjoys the highest kinds of pleasures for eternity must face the critics who point out that such continual pleasure would constitute the most boring and ugly kind of existence. It would in fact constitute a degradation rather than a progress. Heaven help us if Elysium is so hellish!

There is an analogy here with some of our earlier remarks concerning the concepts of agreement and disagreement. The desire that all men agree or the wish to make agreement the basis of truth is very much like the desire that all men be satisfied, and that satisfaction become the basis of the ethics of whole systems. Those who on the other hand propose that truth depends on a kind of disagreement are very much like those who argue that the ethics of whole systems must depend in part at least on concepts of conflict, struggle, and despair.

But have we really reached a point of disagreement between the two positions? If it is true that those who live intensely, that is, express their life in its fullest form, find this expression in dissatisfaction and conflict, can we not incorporate all this into a much more general notion of utility maximization and simply assign a high utility to life's struggles as well as to life's attainments? It is possible that the answer may be yes, because there is no stopping a mind bent on generalizing its ideas. Those who intend to use utility as a basic gauge of the level of a society may be quite willing to take up the challenge of incorporating so elusive a concept as *dis*satisfaction into the whole "model" of social development. And indeed this approach to the ethics of whole systems should certainly be tried.

Nonetheless, the point that has been introduced in the last few paragraphs should not be lost by some vague hope that we can extend the concept of utility in an appropriate manner. In a way, the basic requirement that men live a tragic as well as a comic life goes "beyond good and evil." Good in the sense used in utility theory constitutes a way of estimating the progress of a society in terms of its ability to satisfy man's needs and requirements. Evil gauges the extent to which forces are at work that prevent the realization of so-called rational plans for society. But man's needs for struggle, conflict, tragedy, and despair lie beyond these considerations of good and evil. They lie at the very root of man's biological existence. Man is a living being and needs to express himself in the many forms in which life can be expressed, including both satisfaction and struggle. Hence the biological approach to the ethics of whole systems may be a more appropriate one. Or, since inquiry always proceeds dialectically, both the idea of utility maximization and the idea of the biological analogy should be pushed as far as possible.

What shall we say in the end, then, about the underlying management philosophy of whole systems and the concept of progress? We have had a great deal to say about the many pitfalls that can occur as we try to find ways of measuring social development. We can also recognize that we are very far indeed from any concept of a "level" of society that can be used in a theory of progress and can survive counterarguments of an intelligent, rational intellect. As a consequence, whatever may be the value to the politicians of society in debating whether the West or the East is the more highly developed in its social form, or whether there really are underdeveloped nations, for the intellectual mind none of this debate has much meaning. We have also tried to show that the use of technological development by itself as a criterion of social development is inappropriate. Indeed, technological development by itself is irrelevant with respect to the level of the society. In the end we can say that, although at the present time we lack any basis for intellectual conclusions about the criteria of progress, that is, about the ethics of whole systems, we do have one great strength: an enormous curiosity about the meaning of progress. Coupled with this curiosity is, I think, some optimism that man may attempt at some future time to learn a great deal more about this most deep mystery of the natural world.

Underlying the whole discussion of improvement and progress has been an unstated axiom: "Science," by means of its expertise in discovering truth, will find a way to become an expert on basic human values. In other words, the curiosity we just mentioned is the curiosity of a select group of intellectuals—the system scientists, operations researchers, economists, and the like. These men, says the axiom, may some day become the world's experts on what the basic values of the world are, and they will advise—or even tell—politicians what to do.

That this axiom may be false seems almost axiomatic. There seems to be nothing in the personal life or the intellectual attainments of scientists that would qualify them for this expert role. Some philosophers have claimed that science "by its very nature" cannot determine what "ought to be." Of course this claim itself is rather foolish in that science—viewed as a managed enterprise—is continuously deciding what ought to be in its own domain. The point is that the present enterprise of science, concentrating as it does on very special aspects of nature, probably does not qualify the "science" of today to take on the expert role in determining man's basic values.

But if we are to undertake to judge the basic values and level of progress of society, then who is to make this very important and basic decision? Who—if not the scientist—shall decide whether a society is deteriorating or progressing?

If we answer this question, as many societies have, in terms of an elite or some other form of "aristocracy," we have what Western man in his democracy must regard as the most futile kind of answer. The great mistakes in the political life of men have been made because certain individuals, often with the best intent in the world, have decided they are qualified to judge whether a given development in a society is dangerous or beneficial to man. In the Western side of the world, time after time, men have decided that certain events in the world scene call for intervention, often of a military sort, to prevent further "degradation" of some nation. They have made this decision on their own or on the basis of the recommendation of their expert advisers. Even though one agrees with their concept of degradation, one can well criticize the basis on which the decision was made.

Should a president or premier, congress or parliament, ever have the delegated authority to "decide" how to solve problems of health, poverty, education, civil rights, foreign policy?

Francis Bacon expressed the hope that the decisions about quality of a society could be made by "science," and many of today's political leaders seem to agree with him. All sorts of "scientific panels" are being called to Washington to advise on all sorts of "improvements" in our society. But the question still remains: Are there people in the scientific community who are eminently qualified to make the kinds of decisions that we have been discussing in this chapter? Even though some of the most brilliant minds exist in the scientific community, their brilliance is in terms of scientific discoveries within a discipline and in no sense qualifies them to give "expert" advice concerning policy decisions for the whole society. Brilliance of mind is not a quality that necessarily leads to the best type of judgment concerning the ethics of whole systems. Indeed, there is often an inclination of the brilliant mind to select one aspect of the total situation that can be most precisely formulated and to give this aspect far greater weight than it deserves, simply because it *can* be so formulated in comparison with the other, far more important aspects.

No, we cannot assign the matter of judging a society and formulating policies for it to any kind of elite, be it scientific or managerial. The best answer that men have developed to date to the question "Who shall decide?" is not to be found either within political power or intellectual prowess. It lies in the concept of a well-informed public.

the role
of the
well-informed public

It is always fascinating to read over the pages in which men in the past have tried to express their plans and hopes for the well-being of the human race. No better example of this type of literature is to be found than in Plato's *Republic*. Plato tries to describe the manner in which a social order can be created, where justice reigns and where parts of the social order are so related that the whole plan displays the most beautiful rationality possible.

Since Plato's time, social philosophers have been painting various pictures of the society they deem to be the most perfect, even though they realize that the hope of attaining such a society seems dim indeed. The very name "utopia" suggests this nowhereness of the ideal of rational society.

Even in our own day when men are especially anxious about the doom of the human race, the planning spokesmen still have their day. They point to the need for various types of improvements that they believe are essential for the social system to be a suitable habitat for human life. In addition to freedom of vote and freedom from exploitation, there are other freedoms—from want and disease—that form the rational criteria politicians and planners find to be a basis for their objectives in bringing about an adequate human society.

When we come down from the loftier levels of planning

the society of the entire world to more realistic problems of urban planning and redevelopment, the same rational criteria appear. We have only to look at a city of today to immediately decide what needs to be changed. The most obvious defects of a modern city, it appears, are its slums, lack of sanitation, lack of recreation, lack of educational facilities. And where poverty, for example, shows itself so prominently as it does in slum areas of many cities, the natural inclination of the city planner is to begin to think of the means by which these poverty areas can be removed. Slum clearance is very much like dirt clearance in a household. If the floor is dirty, one should sweep out the dirt. If there are slums in a city, one should sweep out the slums.

Thus slum clearance becomes a prominent feature of many city plans. The underlying idea is that the planner can *at least* accomplish this much. He can remove the obvious inadequacies of city living by removing the areas in which these inadequacies present themselves most clearly. With a modesty that is not always becoming, he calls his approach *incrementalism* to indicate that he does not intend to make big changes, but rather smaller and more obvious ones.

Much the same philosophy appears in the international scene. As a Western statesman looks at a country, he asks himself what are its most serious defects, and if he is imbued with the notions of American political philosophy and believes in the rewards of American technology, he may decide that the country is economically underdeveloped or that its form of government is obviously defective. He will come to believe that the problem of improvement of such a nation consists in increasing its technological capabilities and replacing the government in power by one with more democratic and Western leanings.

So strong is the feeling that specific wrongs should first be removed that, even in the case of the most worthwhile causes, political leaders will insist that since some individuals involved in the support of the causes show the wrong kind of political inclinations, the whole cause is suspect and the first thing to do is remove the undesirables.

What is wrong with incrementalism—the modest attempt to remove a defect in a social system whenever the defect becomes clearly recognizable? The wrongness lies in the logical fallacy familiar to anyone who tries to *apply* principles. Few of us would deny the principle that deprivation in an economy of plenty is wrong, but how should this principle be applied? If we reply that whenever signs of deprivation become obvious to some policy maker in the society, the deprivation should be removed according to this policy maker's concepts, have we really applied the principle? No. Instead we have introduced a second principle which tells us in effect how to apply the first principle. It tells us that the correct way to apply the principle is to ask someone in a position of authority to decide whether there is an unsatisfactory sign of poverty and to decide the correct way to remove the "wrong of poverty."

But this second principle is much too vague. We need now a principle that tells us the characteristics of the person who is to have the authority to decide when "poverty" has occurred and the manner in which it is to be removed. This calls for a third principle that in effect describes the individuals who have authority and responsibility for applying the first two principles. We might say, for example, that an "expert" in urban planning should have the responsibility and authority for recognizing areas of deprivation and the manner in which they are to be corrected. If so, then our third principle would assign this authority and responsibility to such an individual. Needless to say, we would then need a fourth principle to tell us who shall decide whether a given individual meets the requirements set forth in third principle, and how he shall decide.

We are discussing the well-known difficulty of any logical approach to decision making. Logic by its very structure seems incapable of answering the most fundamental problem of decision making. Its only way of facing a difficulty is to state another principle, but no series of principles, however long, will ever establish the notion of application as it appears in the direct action of individuals. That is, logic by itself seems incapable of providing a complete account of how plans are to be carried out in practice in the social order.

The most telling criticism of Plato's *Republic* is not so much the economic, political, and social orderings that he designed into his state, but rather the way in which the plan of the state is to be carried out in terms of responsibility and authority of the citizens. Whether he wished to or not, Plato introduces into his state a self-perpetuating power elite, who in effect decides the application of the educational principles that determine who is to govern and who is to take on the role of the worker and soldier. There is nothing in the *Republic* guaranteeing that such a power elite may not simply define the elegant Platonic concepts of the rational order to their own liking and thus apply in a straightfaced manner the principles of justice to create a social order in which the less-than-desirable elements of society—according to Plato's concept—would govern.

A more recent example is the discussion now prevalent among biologists concerning the breaking of the genetic code. There seems to be an opportunity to determine the code built into a gene that provides instructions for the development of a human being. As a consequence, it is at least conceivable that biologists can determine which genes will produce the "best" individuals from both the biological and the psychological point of view. The obvious but horrifying suggestion is that the human race keep a bank of sperm of "outstanding" persons, thereby guaranteeing that the individuals born in succeeding generations are of the highest caliber. To a rational mind this plan may seem to be a superbly simple answer to the pressing problems of the human race. Such a rational mind would look forward to an age where every living individual is at least of the caliber of the so-called outstanding individuals of our age. Beyond this age is an age of "superoutstanding" individuals and so on to the age of ideal humans. Thereby is guaranteed a planned evolution of the human race.

Why does this kind of thinking on the part of some people appear so horrifying to the rest of us? Why should we not condone a eugenics in which by our own design we create the next generation, a generation free of many of the physical and mental health problems of today?

The answer is simple. *Who* shall decide what "outstanding" means in this context? Shall it be the biologist, according to his criteria of physical and mental health? If so, one shudders to think of the future generations made up of physically and mentally "healthy"

creatures with an immense capacity to destroy each other, simply because they lack the deeper human feelings that constitute the safe-
guards of the ordinary but mentally less adept human being. At the
present time the human race is just about able to cope with the number of outstanding men that exist in a given generation. The "ordinary" man has good reason not to be terribly grateful for the activities
of outstanding men, considering what outstanding men often do to
society. Whether they be scientists, artists, or politicians, the outstanding are often deficient in some fundamental function of the
human psyche, are frequently narrow in their perspective, and indeed
can only be regarded as potentially dangerous individuals by their
fellow humans.

Perhaps the answer is to add some psychologists and psychoanalysts to the Council on Who Shall Survive. But the biologists
and psychologists are politically naïve, as every university professor
knows. Hence we should add some politicians and political scientists
who can plan for the realistic education of the healthy specimens of
the future.

If the selection of the products of the gene bank were handed
over to politicians, then we would have very much the kind of situation we have today with respect to the utilization of atomic energy
for both peaceful and warlike purposes. The next generation of politically realistic strong men might produce an even more stupid international policy than the one we have today.

The idea of the expert planner is frightening. It is a bad idea,
based on the same kind of piecemeal thinking that implies a degradation of human societies. And furthermore there is another, surely
more progressive way to look at the problems of applying rational
principles of planning to the improvement of human society. This
is to recognize what we have been saying all along—that there is
no such thing as improving a part of the system without taking into
account what happens to the whole system as a consequence. To
recapitulate, it may be true as we look around an urban society that
we can easily see areas where people live in poverty, in unsanitary
conditions, without recreational facilities, and so on. The question,
however, is: How should this problem be solved? If the answer is

the naïve one of simply removing slums and other undesirable areas, thus "creating" recreational facilities and sanitary conditions, then have we really "solved the problem" that beset the urban community? The answer in terms of the ethics of the whole system is that we clearly have not. What has happened to urban society as a consequence of slum clearance? Most important, what happened to the inhabitants of the slums? Were they forced to go elsewhere to create even more unsatisfactory living conditions? Were the slums cleared to be replaced by ugly parking lots or rows of boxlike apartment dwellings with all the opportunity of becoming future ghettos of subsequent generations? In their eagerness to clear slums and remove the obvious deficiencies of urban life, have the planners simply forgotten other opportunities for utilization of the scarce resources of the community? Could the funds spent on slum clearance have been far better spent, for example, on increasing the educational power of the community, so that people in the slums as well as other members of the urban community could look forward to a far better-informed public in the next decade?

The point is that a planning principle of the sort we have been discussing so far in this chapter suppresses a very critical phrase, often worded "all other things being equal." The planning principle cannot incorporate all the conditions applicable to the entire system. It must presuppose that the problem has been narrowed to the point where the surrounding relevant conditions have been taken care of by other plans.

This is another way to state the difference between a planning principle and the decision itself. The decision itself necessarily incorporates all the considerations about the entire system—its scarce resources, the consequences of the decision to various other kinds of activities, the various people who will feel the impact of the decision, and so on. The decision, in effect, is the whole plan. Of course this does not mean that the so-called decision maker will necessarily be conscious of all the relevant considerations. It simply means that anyone adequately observing the decision when it occurs can see reflected in it all the kinds of consequence that we have been discussing, that is, can see reflected in it a version of the ethics of the whole system. Therefore the planner, however logical he may be and however appealing and straightforward his plan, simply must fail to cope with the decision itself, because he cannot possibly hope by his planning principle alone to state what in essence is incorporated in the decision, namely, considerations of the whole system.

How can this recapitulation of earlier remarks be used to help us solve the problem of "*who* shall decide?" The answer must be "everybody." But do we really mean that everybody shall have the authority and responsibility to make the important political decisions of today? To Thomas Jefferson's eloquent, "All men are created equal," Alexander Hamilton added, "But they do not stay that way very long." According to Hamiltonian political theory, all men at birth ought to have equal opportunity to become the ones who have responsibility and authority for political decisions, but it is only the aristocrats, that is, the best among men, who shall finally be given the authority and responsibility. What is it therefore that makes a man "aristocratic," that is, best capable in his society of making these decisions?

Clearly the answer on a rational basis is that the well-informed individual is the one who is so qualified.

Now I am not discussing here whether in America or in any other country today we have come anywhere near succeeding in applying the principle that the well-informed public shall have authority and responsibility for national decision making. I am much more interested in what this concept could possibly mean and how one could try to apply it.

In discussions of information, writers sometimes distinguish between information about means and information about ends. They make this distinction because they believe that each person has adequate information about his own needs and wants (that is, his ends) but does not always have information about the means of gaining his ends nor the manner in which a given action will interfere with what another person wants. They say that the experts are supposed to tell us how to get what we want in the most effective way, while the citizen in a democratic society states by his vote what he wants.

But for our present purposes we will probably do better if we forget this familiar distinction. We should forget it anyhow, since by this time in the growth of our psychological knowledge we should be aware that the individual person often doesn't know what he wants or even what he needs. Furthermore, we have been reviewing a number of reasons to suspect the "expert"—scientific, managerial, or professional—about his claim to know the optimal means of society in gaining its goals.

What we seek, therefore, is not some common-sense or widely accepted criterion of the well-informed person, but rather a criterion that will stand up under the scrutiny of rational criticism. The claim that each person is an expert about his own wants, or that the engineer or economist is an expert of bridges or finances, is a common-sense claim that fails to meet the requirement of critical reason.

One obvious though unsatisfactory criterion was mentioned in the chapter on management. It says that the well-informed individual is comparable to a well-informed computer, although possibly having certain abilities not yet attained by computers. Pursuing this analogy, one might go on to say that in the case of any important political decision of society there is a set of relevant data some of which may not yet have been collected. Anyone who has acquired all the relevant information should therefore be thought of as "well informed" because he has stored in his memory all the pieces of information that are available and that are relevant to the decision. In case all relevant information has not been collected, then the well-informed person should be the one with the maximum amount of available information in his memory.

The analogy would go on to claim that any citizen who is "well informed" in the sense just defined should be given the responsibility and authority for decision making, that is, should be given an "equal voice" in the decision-making body.

A number of objections to this analogy can be raised, but before we consider them we might speculate a bit on how a public could ever become well informed in this sense. The most obvious answer is that modern technology has supplied us with new types of mass communication, such as television, radio, telephone, postal service, and so on, and that therefore it is at least feasible for each individual to be presented with relevant information on the major political decisions of our day, because each can have this information immediately available in his environment. There can be no question, I think, that in many of today's societies such opportunities are increasing; mass media are being opened up to display to the citizen many types of information that in previous generations were not available to him. Also the spirit of debate that pervades many societies today permits the intelligent citizen to listen to both sides—to have available the kinds of data that both sides feel are relevant to the decision making.

Now if we turn to some of the objections to this concept of a well-informed public, we can begin by noting that certain individuals are in control of the mass media made available to the average citizen. These persons are the politicians themselves and the owners of various television, newspaper, and other types of communication companies. Since they control the mass media, these individuals are capable of directing the way in which the public pays attention to issues. The question therefore is whether those who control what is presented to the citizen are themselves well informed and whether they act on the basis of information or rather a desire to be leaders and controllers of public opinion

In our society there is a "hidden leadership" which operates by attracting attention of the society to certain issues and consequently neglecting other issues. Thus at one time we are concerned about the possibility of fallout, but a few years later we forget and are excited about juvenile delinquency, then we forget both these issues and worry about brinkmanship, then about civil rights. In all these cases each problem continues to exist—possibly in an even more severe fashion—than it did when the public was paying attention to it. Nonetheless, the direction of public attention is led by certain forces in our society, often unknown forces that heed to no man's will. Consequently, the well-informed citizen is well informed about the issues that the hidden leadership causes him to be well informed about, and he neglects the issues that the hidden leadership causes him to neglect. And there is no guarantee that the hidden leadership itself is well informed, or indeed that it resides in any individual or group.

Next we should recall the ominous phrase "equal vote" or "equal voice" that was introduced in connection with the well-informed citizen. We said that anyone who is well informed about a national issue should be given an equal voice in the decision-making body. Could we really mean this? A citizen might be well informed about a certain political matter, but he might have relatively little interest or concern in it. For example, a professor in Berkeley, California, may have studied the current problems of the city of New York and therefore may be "well informed" about the relevant issues concerning recreational facilities in that city. Should such a citizen have an "equal vote" concerning recreational policies in New York? If we attempt to overcome the obvious negative reply to this question by adding, "equal vote whenever the issues are of concern to the individual," then we run into a very complicated set of conditions that must be studied before deciding whether a citizen is or is not concerned. Who is well informed about the concerns of his neighbor? Indeed, everyone is potentially concerned about the recreational facilities of any city in our age of community interdependence. Nor is it easy to see how one might try to formulate a voting system that weights the concern of an individual without our having some incredible ability to predict his life concerns and those of the people dear to him.

An even more serious objection to making the well-informed citizen analogous to the well-informed computer is the simple observation that anything containing an immense amount of "information" may not be in a good position at all to make decisions. For example, a computer may have stored in its memory a mass of data, but the processing part of the computer may use only a very selected part of this information and may process it many different ways, some of which would be clearly inadequate from the point of view of an intelligent citizen. There is no denying that many people "know" a great deal about a given situation and yet typically ignore most of the information in arriving at their decisions. They do this by introducing their own criteria of relevance. Thus many citizens object to strikes against industrial corporations even though they recognize the "facts" that certain injustices have been perpetuated by the managers and owners. They simply believe that these so-called facts are not clearly so relevant as other types of information concerning the possible implications of the strike with respect to the health of the economy and with respect to what they consider the obvious right of the managers and owners to dictate how the plant should be run.

But if we add the phrase, "provided the citizen correctly uses the relevant information," then we clearly run into the paradox already introduced in this chapter, namely the problem of knowing the whole system.

Added to these objections are two others which are more in line with the theme of this book. First is the point that the acquisition of information concerning a public issue of some importance is extremely time-consuming. We cannot expect that a citizen will be able to spend the time required, for example, to study whether our foreign policy in underdeveloped countries is correct, while at the same time he studies the multitude of educational, recreational, and health problems of his community. Each of these problems, if it were to be studied adequately, would require the full time of a professional researcher for many months. Time is a scarce resource of every individual, and he has every right to insist that some of his time be spent in the development of his own life and the life of his family. Thus the acquisition of information involves a cost, and if we insist that a well-informed citizen is one who has acquired most, if not all, the relevant information concerning an issue, then we are insisting that anyone who has the authority and responsibility of an equal vote in these issues must be someone who is willing to sacrifice so many hours of his time. This would mean that the "well-informed public" consists of those people who have the leisure time and inclination to study issues of political importance. But it is very doubtful whether such a leisure-time public is the one to which most of us would wish to assign the authority and responsibility of political decisions. Their very ability to find such leisure time for the continuing debate about issues makes them suspect.

The obvious answer to this objection concerning the well-informed public is to design a social system in which there is a division of labor. One segment of such a designed society would be given the responsibility of accumulating bits of information about a public problem and would then proceed to analyze this information and reduce it to certain "succinct" items of information. These succinct items would be so critical to the decision that they in effect determine the correct decision.

For example, suppose we are engaged in negotiating a disarmament agreement with a foreign power; it may happen that there are a number of issues that appear relevant at the outset concerning the various consequences of such a decision with respect to other countries. Nevertheless, the argument might run, the predominant consideration has to do with our own safety, because the "expert" may decide that there is real danger of breakdown of agreements and of a sneak war on the part of the foreign power. He might tell us that the only really relevant piece of information is concerned with the probability of such a sneak attack and that this probability is so high that only one kind of agreement is possible, namely, one in which certain types of inspection procedures are permitted. If these are not permitted, he believes the consequences to our national safety may well be disastrous. The overriding piece of information then turns out to be the information about the probability of a sneak attack, and all other considerations in some sense are of minor importance. Therefore, the argument goes, to create a well-informed public, we need only inform them about this probability and its relevance to the safety of our nation, and inform them that all other information is of minor importance.

One can easily sense an objection to this type of arrangement in which authority and responsibility are so divided in the public domain. The average citizen must adopt an attitude of trust and faith toward those who collect information and analyze it. Since he cannot possibly devote the time required to scan all the relevant public issues, he must also adopt an attitude of trust and faith toward those who decide which issues are truly important. He must know therefore that the persons involved in studies of public policy represent the best interests of society as a whole, and that the recommendations they make concerning relevant information are to be relied upon. How could the public possibly have this information about the individuals who conduct the analysis? The answer might very well be: These individuals come from that segment of society that is renowned for its ability to study problems objectively, and who, because of their training, would rarely or never introduce their own personal bias and political preferences into such studies. One might go on to claim that this segment of society is what we recognize today as the academic scientific community.

This whole concept is thoroughly naïve and ignores the central and fundamental aspect of all political decision making repeated thoughout these essays, namely, that the aspects of decision making cannot be separated. If one knows enough about an individual to be convinced that he has not introduced his own bias and his own unsupported conception of how things should be run into his analysis, then one knows so much about him as to be "well informed" on the entire issue.

It should also be noted in passing that neither the U. S. Constitution nor the general idea of "public debate" solves the problems introduced above. The underlying philosophy of the U. S. Constitution is the system of *checks and balances* in which the decisions made by one sector of society are checked by decisions reached by another sector. This system could only work successfully in terms of the ethics of the whole system, were the various sectors of society themselves to become well informed. If the sectors of society are ill informed, then it is difficult to see in what sense they become checks and balances with respect to the decisions of the other sectors. Similarly, the concept of public debate and the allied concept of competition with respect to social power both fail to incorporate what the rational mind demands, namely, an ability of society to reach a decision that is in some sense satisfactory to the whole of society. If men freely compete in a state of ignorance, why should the results of their competition produce a better whole system?

There is still another hope. Perhaps all we need is an ability to know when a given policy breaks down. Thus the citizen becomes "informed" about urban housing policies when riots occur. He becomes "informed" about educational policies when newspapers headline juvenile delinquency and high-school dropouts. He is "informed" about our foreign policy when it so dismally fails. This hope, however, is the most naïve of all, because it assumes that social policies are reversible: One can back the car out of any roadway no matter how steep and slippery. Too much of our information comes too late. By the time the citizen of 1940 became "informed" about conditions in Central Europe, the Nazis had overrun a good part of it. "Should we go to war?" was no longer a relevant question. "Should we have permitted the risk of war?" was a question that came too early for the busy citizen to be aware of it.

We seem to have reached the end of our confrontation of reason and its claim of a right to plan human societies. Every aspect of this claim seems subject to the most severe criticism. All of us cannot help feeling the danger that underlies the attempts of certain of our fellow men to set forth rational plans for the design of human systems. We seem to have no rational basis for accepting our leaders or their experts.

Should we not, therefore, follow the more obvious line at this point and, giving in to the mood of despair that has crept into the writings of these chapters, find other ways in which men can live their lives, where reason does not assume the position that some would claim for it? Specifically, we could follow the Eastern way and recognize that man's true life is his inner life, and that each man by himself, with whatever aids he can gain from his fellow men, should explore what he himself is like. To the extent that he can do so, he should attempt to remove the troublesome features of the technological society of which he is a member. How he is to do this is a matter for his own decision, but he should realize, as Jacques Ellul has put it, the "technological determinism" of modern society, that is, the inevitable way in which technology takes over the environment of society. Once he has recognized this inevitable determinism and underlying evil of technology, he will be in a position to find whatever inner life is possible in such an environment. He will see that nothing he can do can possibly change the direction of technology and the form that society will take.

This is an escape of despair often expressed in the pages of the history of human thought. Epictetus puts it well in his description of the rational slave who, he says, can at least attain freedom of the attitude of his own mind, so that no matter what the master may do, the slave always has the freedom to choose his own attitude if he is so inclined. The masters of today, unlike the tyrants of past ages, are the technological determinants of human life which man has created and which now master him and his whole system.

Of course Epictetus is naïve in his failure to recognize that attitudes of mind are also an outgrowth of one's environment, and it may very well be that the overmastery of technology will deprive man of his ability to escape into the inner life as well as it deprives man of other freedoms he once had.

One may turn instead to the Existentialist notion of action for its own sake, to the idea that every man can express himself in terms of direct action no matter what his society may be like. He does this not for the sake of accomplishing certain results but merely for the sake of expressing life as he lives it.

If men are incapable of finding the principles that might govern a rational plan of the whole society, and if men are incapable of finding any basis on which responsibility and authority can rationally be assigned, must we not turn to one of these antirational themes? Is there anything in the end to be said for reason in the ethics of the whole system?

in praise
of reason

It is time for a change of mood.

The mood dominating the preceding pages has arisen from reason's self-examination of its own capabilities. The mood is one of despair and pessimism concerning the powers of reason to guide men in the design of their social systems. The mood that was threatening us at the end of the last chapter seemed to be one of overthrowing or eliminating the rational as a value in human life—a tragic mood that might lead us to a kind of antirationalism.

First of all, in creating a new mood we should recognize that it was reason itself that discovered the criticism of its own capabilities. So marvelous an ability on the part of a human function to critically appraise its own inadequacies is not to be neglected. No other function of the human spirit has this capability of reason in recognizing the ways in which it is evil as well as the ways in which it is good. The point is so beautifully illustrated in Kant's *Critique of Pure Reason*—a monument of reason's ability to criticize itself and recognize its nature and limitations.

Furthermore, reason sees no basis on which its critical self-appraisal should lead to its own destruction or neglect. One has only to paraphrase the ending lines of that most beautiful poem in praise of reason, Spinoza's *Ethics*, "All rational solutions are as difficult as they are rare," to be inspired to think again about the power of reason and its possible ability to help man formulate the ethics of the whole system.

The mood of despair that came upon us in the last chapter is only an example of all such moods occurring in the creative life of man. Consider, for example, the scientist. The public will admire the results of science and marvel how a man was able to produce so clear and simple a solution to some mystery of Nature. What they will fail to see is that behind the "simple" conclusion lay a tortuous history, when at many points the scientist felt the deepest of despair. Indeed it is commonplace in the life of any scientist to have at one moment a great enlightenment concerning some feature of the natural world and at the next moment to see that the enlightenment solves only a minor aspect of the real problem. He sees that what he had hoped would be a general principle, capable of explaining all, is at best a special principle only partially capable of explaining a minor part. At such moments he could regard the entire enterprise of science to be futile, because he can recognize that for every solution proposed there is created a far greater mystery.

Much the same thing occurs in any creative aspect of human life. One may admire the paintings and musical compositions of great artists and assume that the artists were easily led to the results they produced, without realizing that behind the scenes there was the despair of ever being able to express by human means the deepest feelings of the human race.

No—reason is not to be put aside simply because by its own reflections it has recognized the distance between where it is and where it ought to be.

The reader of these pages who expects, like the reader of a detective story, that in the end we will propose solutions to the perplexing problems that have arisen in the beginning will be disappointed.

Instead, the lesson to be learned from these pages, if any, is that there is work to be done. The lesson is not that we should forsake reason in developing the ethics of the whole system, but rather that we should use the criticisms that reason has directed against itself to determine what needs to be done.

It is simply not in the spirit of this age to lay down the so-called basic principles of the ethics of human life as the ethical writers of the past have done. All such "basic principles" fail in the light of the self-criticism in which we have indulged ourselves in these pages. This is so whether the principles are based on a pleasure-pain calculus, on a code of ethics like the Ten Commandments, or on the much simpler, more expressive forms of Christian ethics as they appear in the love of one man for another. There is no simple and obvious solution to the problems of the ethics and design of social systems, and there is much work to be done if reason is to survive.

What sort of work? In the spirit of these pages, suppose we turn to the work that must be done to create a "science."

I hope it is clear that the so-called science of today is not a science at all with respect to the problems of how men should live. In this sense the empiricist philosopers are correct when they say that science has no concern with what ought to be and is only concerned with what is. However, they are quite mistaken in taking any pride in this way of characterizing modern-day science. If it is true that modern science concentrates its attention on what is, then modern science is simply a defective part of the social organization, and all the dangers that have been discussed in these pages are real dangers. The public, as a consequence, has every reason to suspect the scientific community and its motivations, because this community is by its own confession indifferent to the real underlying problems of human life.

How can we create a science which is meaningful, that is, a science that will use reason to provide guidelines to men in the improvement and maturation of their own lives and of social systems? Can there be a science of the ethics of the whole system?

Well, first of all, I believe we must create a science that does not lie in one sector of society. There are simply no "experts" in the planning of human societies. The so-called experts know less about the planning of human society than does the public, because in each case the expert brings in a thoroughly biased viewpoint; on account of his expertise he is forced to concentrate on only one aspect of the living system. There seems to be no successful way in which the expert of large-scale systems can become a "generalist." There is no such thing as the "universal man" in the area of the ethics of large-scale systems.

Therefore the need for a well-informed public is a true need. The underlying ethical principle here is that every man ought to feel that by his nature he can acquire knowledge about how society should be designed.

Perhaps the matter can be put this way. It is in everyone's nature not only to nourish himself, reproduce, and engage in pleasure-pain activities, but it is also in his nature to create. And it is in his nature not only to create love and hatred, beauty and ugliness, happiness and distress, it is also in his nature to create knowledge and ignorance; that is, to inquire. Unfortunately, in our present-day society we have succeeded in suppressing man's natural instinct to inquire. We do this in many ways, almost as though our whole social effort were intent on suppressing this natural function.

We suppress the instinct to inquire in our design of mass media. Newspapers, magazines, television, and radio simply fail in their important function of assisting men in their natural attempt to learn about the relevant events occurring in the world about them. Our news media are often biased by the policies of corporations and government agencies that determine what kind of information is to be displayed to the public. Perhaps the most evil symptom of this disgrace of modern society is our policy of so-called security which governs the release of important types of information to the public. Here again the fallacy of concentrating on a part of the system becomes apparent. In defense of security, the government official will point out that if certain types of information are released to the public, they can be made available to undesirable elements of our society as well as to our enemies in other nations. On this ground they are willing to go to any length to prevent the citizen from becoming informed, thereby neglecting the problems of the whole system to perfect their performance in their own sector of society. Information thus comes to be a kind of modern form of value exchange. He who holds information that someone else does not have is regarded to be "richer" than that other person and consequently is in a more powerful position. One does not have to spend many days in Washington before recognizing that the various government agencies do indeed translate information into coinage, and introduce their own security measures concerning the information they hold, so other agencies cannot "steal" the information. In this policy they are aided and abetted by the Congress, which in effect by its own hearings encourages the kind of secrecy that is so insidious in our government. Add to this ineptness in handling information the immense files kept by the FBI and other police agencies, and one comes to recognize that our society has succumbed to the vile disease of clogged information processing.

The disease has spread on the more general level into our educational system. The attitudes of teachers about their specific scientific disciplines are evidence of our gross deficiency in creating the spirit of inquiry in ordinary men. The manner in which materials are presented in the classroom and in the literature quickly convinces a student that he will never understand the underlying principles of more than one discipline of science. The psychologist sees that he cannot possibly understand what the mathematician, physicist, chemist, or biologist is talking about, and therefore gives up in despair. He cannot see the point of attempting to understand the product of these disciplines, nor could he hope to interpret the product in terms of creating a better society. Even where some of our journals rise to a much higher plane in their aspiration to educate the citizen about science, they still regard him as a third-class student in relation to the "great" scientist.

Perhaps one of the most ridiculous manifestations of the disciplines of modern science has been the creation of the so-called social sciences. Enough evil was done in dividing the physical sciences into various kinds of specialized disciplines. The social scientists above all should have recognized the deficiencies of such an organition of their society and refused to let themselves be organized into the same kind of disciplinary structure that the physicists created. Of course they have failed in their attempt to gain disciplinary status and rightfully are regarded with suspicion not only by other scientists on university campuses but also by politicians, who in principle should be eager to make use of their findings had they any value.

Instead of social science partitioning itself into special disciplines, it should recognize that social science is not a science at all unless it becomes a natural part of the activities of social man. All intelligent members of society should form the membership of the social-science discipine, because the social sciences should be considering all the basic problems that need to be studied for the creation of satisfactory ethics of the whole system. Above all, academics should give up the intolerable and inapplicable principle that "good" research can only be conducted by "excellent" researchers. To paraphrase the philosopher, a researcher is not a special kind of person; rather every person is a special kind of researcher. If we were to begin anywhere in this enterprise of eliminating the uncalled-for snobbery of the academic, we should look to the young; how can we get high-school students interested in doing social science? We can't if we say that these students are not competent or "well-enough trained" (as though we knew what adequate training really is).

One of the most absurd myths of the social sciences is the "objectivity" that is alleged to occur in the relation between the scientist-as-observer and the people he observes. He really thinks he can stand apart and objectively observe how people behave, what their attitudes are, how they think, how they decide. If his intent were to be the clown rather than the objective scientist, we could appreciate him more, because in some ways his own behavior and the manner in which he describes the behavior of others is hilarious.

Instead of the silly and empty claim that an observation is objective if it resides in the brain of an unbiased observer, one should say that an observation is objective if it is the creation of many inquirers with many different points of view. What people are really like is what people with the strongest of inquiring motivations will perceive themselves to be like. The "verification" of a scientific finding resides in the creative spirit of human inquiry carried to its maximum potential.

We are not saying that every man will become an "expert" on every political issue of his own local government, of his nation, and of the world. This, as we have shown in the previous chapter, is a hopeless task. But it is important that every man feel a strong inclination to inquire about those things that are of concern to him. We should create an environment in which people will feel that they can behave creatively and with insight in the study of the serious problems of our sociey.

Instead, as we have said, everything in our society seems to run in the opposite direction. The data fed to the public are dull and often false, irrelevant, or confusingly presented. There is nothing inspiring whatsoever in finding out which public official should be elected to a given position, especially when the candidates running for office are both obviously inadequate and both fail to present the public with any basis on which the public could decide. There is little of interest in the average citizen's becoming deeply involved in problems, say, of water allocation or the use of weapons against dangerous forces, because he realizes that anything he does will have absolutely no effect on the decisions that will be made. This is made clear to him over and over again by public officials, by the press, by the many books and magazine articles written on various subjects of critical importance. Even in the rare instances when the public is able to get a glimpse of a debate between two so-called important public officials, like the Kennedy-Nixon shows, the debate appears to be rigged or else so poorly designed that the public can only regard it as an amusing incident that temporarily substitutes for the even more boring programs of the television screens.

Furthermore, as we have said, we live in an age in which political leadership can be accomplished simply by directing public attention to various issues. In effect, our age is an age of extraverted politics. Concern over public policy arises in the environment outside the individual and is not generated by his own internal reason. Indeed, if he has an internal concern that is at variance with the "popular interests," there is nothing whatsoever that he can do about the matter. If the mass media no longer pay attention to problems of fallout or labor exploitation, the average citizen cannot possibly accomplish anything no matter how deep his own feelings may be.

There is much that could be done to transform our mass media into exciting and very inspiring forms of debate. A better design of mass media could be carried out by rational methods, by means of psychological and social information already available to motivate men to inquire about issues. The ordinary man should not have to go to one paper and then another to try to understand what the "two sides of the issue" are. Instead it should be the responsibility of society to provide by means of rational design the strongest kind of debate concerning important political issues.

I am trying to imagine a society in which every man would feel that he could of his own choice become well informed on whatever issues he feels are important. It would be a society in which "brilliance" and "deep insight" are not the hallmarks of the decision makers; it would be a society in which the expert or the astute politician would no longer rule. In such a society every man would feel that one outcome of his interest in important social problems would be his ability to "do something about the matter." Instead of making it clear to the public that nothing they could possibly do will make any difference, the public would feel that they very definitely have ways of expressing themselves to their government as well as to the rest of their fellow men. No man would feel he was merely the observed, rather than the observer; no man would feel he was merely the public, rather than the politician. Technology obviously could be of assistance in such a program if it were designed to do so. For example, the technologically ugly computer might be converted into a more cheerful member of society. Instead of its merely processing information for military command-and-control and defense of our nation, it could be used to store the reactions of the public to various kinds of social issues. Even if we keep our present form of government, our legislators could become well informed about how the public have reacted to the intelligent and exciting debates concerning the major issues they face. In our present society our legislators are not well informed about the public at all.

Off and on in these pages I have talked in what must seem a disparaging way about "great minds" and "outstanding men," because I have felt that this is one of the great fallacies of man's concept of the level of development of a society. Just as technological change is irrelevant in the considerations of the ethical value of the whole, so is the existence of great minds. It is foolish to believe that there are great minds that should have the predominant voice in the management of our society. The great-mind concept is just another illustration of the emphasis on one part of the system, and the failure of the ethical principle of great minds is simply the failure to recognize that an "outstanding part" may have extremely detrimental implications so far as the whole system is concerned.

Of course, intelligence and intellectual ability are important features in an inquiring system, but so are all the creative impulses and deep human feelings that people have.

Here is another way to state the theme we have been developing: In the so-called science we have today there is not enough of the feminine, just as clearly there is not enough of the feminine in our management today. Of course, "masculine" and "feminine" are vague terms, perhaps just because they are of fundamental importance in the human psyche. It is enough to say that the masculine often displays itself in direct action. The masculine attempts to lay out a specific form of things in accordance with a plan, whereas the feminine so often expresses the vaguer aspects of life, its feeling side, its loveliness, its antagonisms. Inquiry in our society has turned out to be so masculine that it is predominantly influenced by concepts of precision, rigor, and accuracy, all characteristic of the masculine side of life. If inquiry is to become a more natural aspect of each person's life, it is essential that it also incorporate the vague, the feeling, and the lovely. The failures of reason that we explored in earlier chapters are the failures of masculine reason.

A good example of the difference between the masculine and the feminine in science is to be found in the theory of experimental design. In the classical theory of experimental design it is essential that the scientist decide beforehand what question he wishes to pose, and that he carefully define his concepts about what he observes. He is required throughout a well-controlled experiment to keep his purpose constant, and he is required not to change the meanings of his concepts. In some real sense, however, these requirements are unnatural. In the more natural mode of inquiry we rarely make our purposes clear, and we rarely keep the meaning of our concepts the same throughout the process of inquiring. A more natural experiment for many people may be the "elusive experiment" in which the process of experiment makes clear the purposes of experiment and aids us in developing the meanings of the terms we use.

In addition to learning a great deal more than we know at present about the nature of inquiry, that is, the natural way in which men inquire, there is also much work to be done in increasing our information about man himself and especially about his needs and wants. Instead of merely fighting Communism, the Western world should be devoting a major part of its research effort to determining why Communism occurs, that is, why certain societies have to express themselves in this manner. And the Eastern world should be devoting a major part of its research effort to trying to understand what makes the Western man so much of a competitive, industrialized creature.

In the end I come to the conclusion that emotion and mood are not the opposite of reason. The plans that men develop for their life are based upon the underlying moods that characterize each living human being, just as, hopefully, they are based upon the reasoning that each man will be able to put into the consideration of the most pressing problems of the human race. To separate mood and reason is as ridiculous as to separate any aspects of the whole system that we live in.

Reason has failed as a human function only because of what men have made of it and not because of what it is in itself. It is the most glorious release of the human spirit. It is that which provides man with the capability of understanding himself, of appreciating his own powers as well as his own deficiencies, of becoming human. It is broad in its perspective; it sweeps over the whole of the problems of the human race, it is the most magnificent endowment that nature has made available to man. It cannot be expressed in terms of simplified "axioms of rational behavior," and it is a serious mistake to think that those who devote their lives to the study of such axioms are in any sense expressing the meaning of rationality.

The astute reader will long ago have recognized that the writing of this chapter has fallen into the same difficulties that earlier chapters have pointed out concerning all rational planning. Some principles have been set forth, some "shoulds" about the ethics of the whole system, without in any way suggesting how the difficulties posed in earlier pages can be solved. Even if we recognize that inquiry should become a more integral part of the life of the human being, how should this principle be applied? *Who* is to decide on its application? *Who* is to decide what inquiry means? *Who* is to decide that the principle itself has any particular validity for men? Indeed, how is such a principle even to be considered by the current decision makers of our society? What would force them in any way to consider the principle seriously, even if it were a valid one? These problems are the problems of self-reflection, which is the basic problem of man's rational life.

Indeed, reason is that function of man that enables him to look at himself and to raise questions about everything he does. Part II explores what this remark might mean.

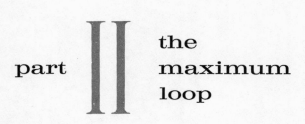

part II the
maximum
loop

rational
decision making

Although Part I ended in praise of reason, it said little (except indirectly) about the nature of rational decision making. It is now time to attempt a clearer definition.

The concept of reason will be forever elusive for mankind, because we can never hope to pin down so important a concept in terms that will be satisfactory forever. The many meanings of reason that we have inherited from our philosophical forebears are inadequate in our present age, and any definition of reason that we attempt to develop now will be unreasonable for the next generations.

Suppose we look at the meaning of these comments carefully, first by discussing some ideas about reason that we have inherited and, second, by considering a somewhat radical idea of what reason could come to mean in our present age.

Of the many meanings given to the concept of reason, perhaps the most predominant in the history of thought has been a definition of reason that has tied it closely to logic.

The general idea here is that reason consists of logical and consistent sets of steps that go from first principles to rigidly derived conclusions. The steps satisfy all the requirements that formal logic imposes on the so-called reasoning process.

This idea has manifested itself in the history of thought

in many ways. One of the most fascinating is Spinoza's *Ethics,* which begins with certain axioms about existence and derives therefrom a whole plan of behavior of the human being. Philosophers from time to time have tried to use Spinoza's axiomatic method in developing more up to date and more satisfactory logics that would help man to decide how his life should be conducted. These are called *rational decision-making models.*

Now few would deny that logic forms a very important part of any definition of reason; nevertheless we should realize that logic in no way constitutes the sufficient condition for rationality. We have already seen that formal logic is at best a way of organizing our thinking process, and the organization itself depends on "managerial principles" that are not captured by formal logic. These managerial principles are to be construed as a part of the rational process and logic cannot be considered to provide the whole story. Furthermore, most of us are probably now convinced that formal logic can by no means provide the kind of "starting principles" that Spinoza found satisfactory in the writing of his *Ethics* several centuries ago.

So much for "formal logic." As I say, it cannot provide sufficient content for the meaning of reason.

On the other hand, philosophers have often extended the meaning of logic to cover many things that the formal logician does not consider. Hegel, for example, in his writings in the last century described logic as the whole process of developing an understanding of the world. This idea of logic was captured in his dialectical method. Similarly, scientists often use the term *logic* to refer to the methods by which they reach their conclusions in their empirical investigations, and they frankly confess that these methods go beyond the rigorous principles of formal logic. Indeed, Karl Popper calls one of his books *The Logic of Discovery,* thereby implying that there is an underlying process in the way in which the scientist comes upon new insights, and also implying that formal logic does not capture all there is to say about logic itself.

When logic is used in this more general sense, it becomes difficult to know whether we should identify logic and reason. But we can agree that the extensions of logic as they occur, for example, in Soviet writings, or the present discussions of the logic of discovery, encompass only a part of the process of rational decision making discussed in the earlier part of this book.

On the basis of these remarks, we can also agree that reason is not equivalent to what might be called calculation; for example, the processes carried on by a computer do not express all there is to be said about the concept of reason.

No more is reason to be identified with "thinking" in the sense in which the concept of thinking is used in modern psychology. C. G. Jung in his *Psychological Types* developed the idea that the human mind could be thought of as displaying four functions: thinking, intuition, sensation, and feeling. Here he clearly recognized that reason or rationality is a broader concept than thinking, because he states that both thinking and feeling are "rational" functions. It seems from his book as though he regards thinking to be more closely allied to formal logic or to calculation than is feeling which, as he describes it, is an evaluating function. Apparently Jung conceived of thinking as the ways in which the mind tries to organize its concepts, while feeling provides the ways in which the mind tries to evaluate the various situations in which it finds itself. On the other hand, Jung does say that sensation and intuition are "nonrational," and in this regard he has gone along with similar kinds of thinking that have occurred in existentialism, in oriental philosophy, and in many other expressions of philosophy in modern days. In all these cases, there has grown up a kind of pride in the antirational, as though the rational represents only a segment of the human life, and as though much is to be said for that part of life which is nonrational or even opposed to reason.

The reader will have gathered from the statements of the first Part that I think such philosophies constitute an unsatisfactory narrowing of the concept of reason. Indeed, the meaning of reason goes beyond any of the so-called functions in Jungian terms; it characterizes the whole of life including the functions of intuition and sensation. Reason has to do with the way in which human beings understand what human life means.

Suppose, instead of discussing further how psychologists and philosophers define reason, we turn to the planners, to the economists, management scientists, and their like. The experiences of these people provide a rich insight into the meaning of reason; maybe the different opinions we will find about the meaning of reason among the planners will provide us with a basis for trying to develop an adequate definition.

In societies with powerful ruling classes it is easy to define rational planning. Reason is taken to be the set of principles that keep the ruling class in power, much as reason in any patriarchal household is the principle that "Father knows best." Reason comes to be the basis of planning as it is dictated by the power elite of a society.

It is this concept of reason of course that modern man has repeatedly tried to deny. Instead he has generated a concept of rational planning that arises not from the power elements of a society but from man's own inner convictions.

To develop this idea of rational planning, the management scientists have followed a long tradition in philosophy, economics, and other disciplines, of attempting to set down in a fairly precise way the "rational rules of behavior." The attempt is quite similar to the idea that the meaning of reason is to be found in logic, but now the axioms express rules of behavior rather than rules of dealing with ideas and symbols.

Some management scientists actually believe that certain of these rules of rational behavior are invariant, that is, they will never change no matter how human conditions themselves may change. They are, in fact, something like the so-called invariant rules of logic which many philosophers in the past believed to be rules of thinking that must apply no matter what the context.

What does such a rational rule of behavior look like? Consider an individual capable of clearly expressing his preferences between certain states of nature. For example, he might be able to say that he prefers listening to a symphony concert to watching a grade-B western movie. He not only says he has this preference, but we will allow for the moment that there is sufficient evidence that this preference as he has expressed it, is correct, so we know what things he prefers to other things. The rational rules of behavior describe how these preferences should be related one to another.

For example, suppose the individual does prefer symphony concerts to western movies, that is, that he prefers A to B. Next, suppose that he prefers western movies to sitting alone at home at night, so that, for example, if there are no symphony concerts and there is a western movie showing at the corner, he would prefer to go to the movie rather than be left alone to his own devices in his own living room. Let's call being left alone to his own devices in his own living room "C". Now we know this much about our hero: he prefers A to B, and he prefers B to C. The rule of behavior in this case states that, if he behaves rationally, he *must* prefer A to C, that is, he must prefer going to a symphony concert over sitting at home alone in his own living room. By the rules of rational behavior, we expect him to voice this preference. But if now we discover that he expresses a preference of C to A, that is, that he prefers sitting alone to going to symphony concerts, then according to the management scientist, such an individual is irrational, or "inconsistent." He is irrational because, although he prefers A to B and B to C, he nonetheless prefers C to A.

Of course the management scientist recognizes that people do display irrational behavior, and indeed in many preference tests that are given, say, in consumer market surveys, customers often show such "irrationalities" when presented with paired comparisons of products. Thus the market surveyor may show product A and B and ask the customer which he prefers, and the consumer will check A. The surveyor later on shows B and C, and the customer checks B. Subsequently the surveyor shows C and A, and the customer "irrationally" checks C. An explantion for this behavior may be easy to find. The customer may have changed his earlier preferences, or he may have really preferred all three equally. The axiom of rational behavior we are considering is not concerned with lapses of memory on the part of the individual, nor is it concerned with inaccurate expressions of preference when the individual is not sure what he really wants. The axiom states that if someone truly prefers A to B and *B* to *C*, then it would be irrational of him *truly* to prefer *C* to *A* "in the same circumstances at the same time." The need to add specifications to the simple rational rule reminds us of the need to elaborate the "law of contradiction" in Part I to the point where the "law" began to lose its meaning.

Other axioms of rational behavior will readily occur to anyone who thinks about the matter. For example, if someone prefers *A* to *B*, he should not simultaneously prefer *B* to *A*.

Why should we regard such axioms to be rational? And why should we believe that these axioms must hold no matter where the individual may be, no matter what may happen to future generations of man?

In addition to reminding us of the struggles to find the laws of logic, the axioms also recall attempts to define moral precepts such as one finds in the Ten Commandments. "Thou shalt not lie" is a precept that was supposed to classify all behavior of a certain kind as immoral and therefore, presumably, irrational. The Ten Commandments are therefore ten necessary conditions for determining whether conduct is rational. Such moral precepts are with us today, but few management scientists would say that these older offerings constitute a reliable basis for defining rational decision making. We have come to suspect that each Commandment has its exceptions, and that unless these exceptions are carefully listed and founded on more fundamental concepts of reasoning, there is no justification for accepting any Commandment by itself as a partial definition of rational behavior. Thus most of us believe that it is perfectly all right to lie or kill on occasion, especially when lying or killing will increase the probability of our own survival or of our nation's survival.

Some philosophers have attempted to overcome the difficulties of rigorous rules of moral conduct by suggesting more "basic" principles, such as the principle that every man ought to preserve his own happiness, but now the rule is far too vague to apply. Furthermore, the rule does not even seem to be valid in cases where a person prefers to sacrifice his happiness for the sake of some more desirable goal, for example, the safety of his loved ones. For this reason the management scientists have tried to seek more basic principles of rational conduct.

One of the more fascinating developments of principles of rational conduct has occurred in *game theory*—a theory that tries to describe rational conduct in the context of conflict. It sets forth "rational" rules governing "fair play" and tries to discover optimal strategies that can be followed by an individual when he is facing his opponent in a situation governed by certain recognizable rules.

The reader will readily find two very serious objections to the management scientist's approach to rational decision making. On the one hand, he will come to feel that even though it may be true that these axioms define rational behavior, nevertheless they cover so little of practical importance that their contribution to the meaning of rationality is very small indeed.

For example, we would all like to know the rational way of solving some of the persistent international problems of our day. We would also like to be able to recognize rational urban and regional development plans. We would like to know how to allocate our water resources. We would like to know how rationally to design our educational systems, and so on. It doesn't seem to help us a great deal to know that if we prefer A to B and B to C, then A is preferred to C. Also, it does not seem to help us very much to follow the rules prescribed by game theory. These rules still leave so much open that they hardly seem sufficient to provide a basis for planning.

Nevertheless, this objection in some sense misses the point. What the management scientists are saying is that if we are able to collect reliable information concerning preferences, then by means of the axioms of rational behavior, we will be able to identify *the* set of optimal plans. In other words, the axioms of rational behavior provide the way of processing the basic information for rational plans, provided that information concerning preferences is available.

A more serious objection to the management scientist's notion of rational behavior is to question whether these axioms of rational behavior tell us anything at all. Indeed, they may simply follow from their own definition of preference. The question therefore is whether their definition of preference is a suitable basis for defining rationality. It is much as though the management scientist were telling us that this is how preference "ought rationally" to be defined, without his attempting at all to justify his own beliefs. And indeed in many of the writings of the management scientists, one finds a strong inclination of the authors to use their own personal attitudes as a justification of what they say about the rules of rational behavior. What they are saying is that if a man prefers A to B according to *their* concept of preference, and B to C according to their concept of preference, then he must prefer A to C according to their concept of preference. They are not telling us whether their concept of preference is a suitable one.

How could one object to the management scientists' concept of preference? Why, one could object to it because one might find it completely irrelevant with respect to the notions of rationality. We have been repeatedly hinting in this discourse that rationality has to do with goals as well as the means of the attainment of goals. But the concept of rationality as expressed in the rules of behavior mentioned above tells us nothing about whether the goals are rational or irrational. Indeed, these rules of behavior are as applicable to the policies of a criminal or a dictator as they are to the policies of an enlightened society. They would tell a criminal the best way to rob a house; they would tell a dictator the best way to eliminate a minority group; in each case the optimal way to evil is to act "in accordance with rational rules of behavior." Indeed, if preference is used in such a broad way as the so-called rules of rational behavior imply, it is doubtful whether preference so used has anything to do with rational planning.

For this reason, as we indicated in the earlier chapters, it seems desirable to introduce into the concept of rationality other considerations than a mere preference ordering.

These considerations have to do with the meaning of Nature itself. The idea here is that Nature "expresses" a type of rationality and that we should seek to discover what is the rational in Nature so that each may adapt what he had found to his own behavior. Of all the places that men may seek to find clues concerning the rationality of Nature, perhaps the best is in the behavior of the members of the living species. The rationality of an insect, of a bacterium, of an animal, expresses some aspect of the total rationality of Nature itself.

Hence scientists have attempted to explore the nature of the living to gain thereby some clues concerning the way in which human lives can be rationally conducted. In some cases, they have also explored the nature of the nonliving—the physical universe— to search for clues concerning rationality. Thereby in recent years we have been exposed to cybernetics, in which the "well-adjusted" physical system becomes the prototype of all living rational behavior.

This theory of rationality made a lot of sense to the biologists of the nineteenth and the twentieth centuries. It also makes sense to today's evolutionary industrial theorists. Modern industry began with very crude machinery, crudely operated. After a while men learned how to build better machines, but they neglected the living standards of the worker. After a while they were forced to recognize the worker's claims, but they couldn't determine how to use him efficiently. Along came industrial engineering and efficiency went up. Along came automation, and it went up even more. Along came operations research and management science and even greater refinements were introduced. At each stage we redeveloped our notion of rational industrialization. Today we don't hesitate to say that the manager who ignores worker rights or uses old methods of manufacturing is "backward," that is, "irrational." We think he is backward or irrational because what he is doing comes earlier in the evolutionary process of industrialization than what is now done. Hence our use of terms like "underdeveloped nations." We all expect that the industrial leaders and scientists of a generation hence will consider us to be backward. How irrational our methods will appear to the inhabitants of the twenty-third century!

It's all very happy thinking, this evolutionary concept of rationality, but it also has much about it that seems naïve. At times the whole philosophy appears to be saying that any change is a good change, even if automation leads many citizens into economic disaster, even if technology destroys individual creativeness, even if science blows us all to our doom. Get on with the industrial evolution regardless of where it leads us, at all costs! Whatever change is proposed, do it!

Can we really expect that "Nature" will provide us with the clues of rationality? Isn't this way of putting the matter absurd? It assumes that Nature is a kind of Great Mother, who, if we listen to her carefully, will provide us with the lessons that we need to conduct our lives correctly. There is no question, of course, that in the popular discussions of science people do talk about Nature in exactly this way, and psychologists would probably have no difficulty in pointing out that the people who do talk this way are much influenced by some kind of mother complex. Game theorists, for example, often describe experimentations as a "game with Nature," as though Mother Nature sat across a board and made certain moves, which were then observed by the experimenter, who then tried to cope with Mother Nature's moves in some appropriate rational fashion. It may be that we learn from Nature a great deal, but the lesson of Immanuel Kant should never be forgotten, that whatever rationality we may "find" in Nature, we have put there ourselves, simply because Nature is our own creation. It is in fact our description of what the largest system is like.

I said at the outset I would try out a more radical approach to the meaning of reason. Naturally this is done with all the hesitations that go along with radical approaches. This approach at best can only be regarded as a kind of working hypothesis. It is a suggestion based on much that was discussed earlier in this book about the ethics of the whole system. When discussing management and science, I kept saying to myself over and over again that science could be looked at as a kind of management, or that management could be looked at as a kind of science. Saying that science can become a way of managing didn't imply automation or any other form of mechanical decision making, because none of this is science. Science is the creative discovery of knowledge. Management science is the process of trying to look at science as a management function. Similarly, management can be looked at as a scientific function, that is, as a way of finding out about the world.

The end of the last chapter stated that reason is the process by which man is able to look at himself, but it should be added that the way anything can look at itself is through a series of frameworks. The conclusion is that a social institution becomes rational to the extent that it can be considered to function like some other institution. Thus, management becomes rational to the extent that it can be viewed as science, and science becomes rational to the extent that it can be viewed as management. So, too, for the other important social institutions. Religion becomes rational to the extent that it can be viewed as a science, or as a management. And management becomes rational again in the way in which it can be viewed as a religion. The evolution of the rationality of politics will also include the development of politics as a science, as a management, as a religion, as an educational system. Hence what we were discussing in the chapter on the well-informed public turns out to be a proposal to make politics more of an educational system, that is, to develop a political life of our society in which politics will create the well-informed public.

Much needs to be said to make this idea of rationality clearer and more convincing. It is an idea that borrows from the philosophy of reason in Nature, but tries to overcome the more passive aspects of evolutionary philosophy. It says that man becomes more rational to the extent that he becomes reflective. But reflection is not merely a "looking inward"; it is not a direct self-examination. Rather, the rationality of reflection comes from using as much of the world, or the "whole system," as one possibly can to understand oneself.

If we say that the manager should think of himself as a scientist, we do not mean that he should try to become a scientist according to today's standards. For today's science is not reflective: It has a very narrow view of what it is. Today's science is not very rational. But if management could be considered as a science, then management would change, and so would science. Both would become more rational. The way in which management can be viewed as science opens up our eyes to the deeper meanings of science.

It is impossible to determine the rationality of conduct in one framework alone, as those who try to develop basic axioms of rational behavior attempt to do. Nor is rational conduct simply a development along certain prescribed lines, as evolutionary theory suggests. The test of the rationality of an institution, or a company, or a person, is the determination of the manner in which X functions as Y, and the way in which Y functions as X. For something to be able to look at itself, it must look at itself as though it were something other. What is not explained is the meaning of "function as." What is entailed in "considering" management as science, or science as management? In the end, the answer will probably be, "I'm not sure." But a few explorations of the idea in the chapters that follow may help to clarify as well as to confuse.

the x of x

The world of decision making seems to be ever expanding—in scope and in complexity. Each major decision appears to have endless ramifications in the lives of men of today and tomorrow's days.

We would love ever so dearly to understand our own decision making. We sense all too well that it is a phenomenon far more mysterious than the phenomena of matter, or of life, or of space.

The peculiar thing is that we humans created decision making and the many different edifices of decisions: the company, the university, the government. We conceive ourselves to be the creators of these wonders of Nature, but we don't understand them. Our creations have become complicated and uncertain. Even our most astute mathematical analysis uncovers only a very small bit of the true structure of man-made organizations.

It is almost as though because we build these things, we don't want to know what they are like. Men turn their intellecual attention in the main to phenomena they did not create—the physical and the organic world. It may be that we suspect the dangers of investigating our own creations in depth. The investigation may well be at the cost of revealing the basic evil of man's ways.

The suspicion is a sound one, as all the wise men of history have told us. He who seeks to understand himself seeks the devil in himself as well as his God. The view that his understanding will open up may be too much for his contemplation, for it may display to him what he really is: perhaps the agent of all that is decadent in Nature.

Almost a decade ago a courageous designer of constitutions wrote that he hoped a new Institute of Management Science would strive for a "unified science of management." I do not know whether this man was waggish or wise. He may have felt that there was something of the subtle joke in suggesting that science could ever become astute enough to understand how men manage. Or he may have felt that the time had come at last for men to understand their own decision making, even at the risk of thereby discovering their own ineptitude.

To understand oneself is the problem of reflection. It is the fundamental problem of philosophy. We call it the self-reflective, or self-referencing problem. It keeps reappearing in all the ages of history—in all its intellectual pursuits. It is exciting to explore, it is frustrating to try to solve, it is deadly serious in its import.

Consider, if you will, that most fascinating discipline called logic. Logic is the caretaker of man's reason. Without logic we are all insane. The hallmark of reason is consistency. The hallmark of consistency is redundancy. If I say "p is true" then this implies "p is true." To give up such a straightforward principle of reasoning is to give up all grounds for thinking. A proposition must imply itself— at least—and above all.

What's wrong with this? It merely says that a proposition reflects its own truth, a beautiful way to say the most prosaic thing we know. What can disturb the equanimity of logical perfection? Why, a Cretan can. This Cretan—call him Epimenedes—says that all Cretans are liars. More specifically, he says, "I am now lying." If he is truly referring to his own veracity, he must be truly telling us that he lies, in which case he truly tells us that he is untruthful. If he is falsely referring to his own veracity, he must be falsely telling us that he lies, in which case he untruthfully tells us that he is truthful. Seemingly, we must forbid Epimenedes to speak about his own lying. But we will permit him to say that a true proposition implies itself. Can we forbid the one and permit the other? Anyone who has studied the problem knows the tortuous pathways that must be constructed to keep our logic sane: the theory of types, the fundamental inability of arithmetic to prove its own consistency. To some it comes as a distinct shock to realize that even in today's enlightened world, we still do not fully understand what it means to be consistent: We may not understand the consistency of consistency, or the sanity of being sane.

Turn now to another example. A careful man is measuring a length. Curious, we ask him how he knows that the figures he reports are reliable. He replies by describing to us the process by which he has calibrated his instruments. As he takes us, step by step, back to the standard meter rod, we cannot help but suspect that he has assumed that which he wants to prove. His calibration methods involve measuring temperature. But the normal methods of measuring temperatures involve comparisons of the length of a rod of mercury, for example. Hence to measure length accurately one must assume that he can measure length accurately.

How can a system, of measurement or any other kind of production, tell itself that it is performing adequately? The question is certainly a subtle one, no matter how often one repeats the negligent answer, "because it works." Actually, those who say "because it works" don't want to consider the issue. If they did, they would have to ask, "how do I know it works?" They might then answer, "because no one complains." If they did, they would have to understand why people complain. And *that* problem would be beyond their patience.

We are all familiar with one answer to the problem of a system's telling itself that it is performing adequately. This answer consists of modeling the system using an input, an output, and a feedback device. In very general and somewhat vague terms, the feedback tells the system how it is performing. It normally does this by means of an analysis of the output, based on imposed criteria of statistical stability.

Everyone recognizes that such systems are only partially self-reflective. If the input is regarded to be part of the system, it is safe to say that the system does not fully understand itself; it does not understand its own input. If the criteria of stability are imposed from outside, the system does not understand its own criteria.

These remarks are merely challenges to the system designer. If the inputs might turn out to be unsatisfactory, then design the system so it can scan the quality of the input. Thus, if the human programmer of computers makes many mistakes, then get the computer to query the programmer. Better still, get the computer to program itself. And if the computer can't tell whether an output has any value, get the computer to understand its goals and to query the user whether the problem is a sensible or useful one. Better still, get the computer to create its own problems.

How far will this design process go? Will the computer become a self-conscious scientist—even more self-conscious than present-day scientists (which is really not very self-conscious at that)?

This question, of course, suggests the next example of the self-reflective problem: the understanding of "adaptive systems." Adaptive systems are systems that can react to their own performance, that is, can judge the effectiveness of their choices, and learn to do better next time. The crucial points in the life of an adaptive system are the moments when it says, "I like it" or "I don't like it." The system lives by making exploratory tries, and evaluating the outcomes. If it doesn't like the outcome, and yet survives, it will try another pathway. Eventually, it may find some pathway that is satisfactory. If so, it sticks to it, the "it" being one course of action or perhaps a mixed strategy of actions.

The adaptive system is not a reflective system. It only becomes so when it first whispers to itself, "Why don't I like it?" Sometimes the answer that is forthcoming is very simple and direct; for example, "I don't like it because I lost," or "I don't like it because it hurts." In the first case, the system recognizes externally imposed conditions of winning and losing. It doesn't understand why it wins or loses, or even what winning or losing means. In the second case, the system has an inbuilt pain and pleasure response. If there is pain, "it" isn't all right. If there is pleasure, "it" is all right. This is the childish adaptive system, beautiful in design, highly effective in its limited environment. Nature's gift is pain, a resource of infinite value in a world of complicated dangers. As the child becomes an adolescent, he typically will ask, "What's wrong with pain?" He will be asking the next question of reflection, and he may well explore, or be forced to explore, the possibilities of adapting to pain. It is the initiation to manhood—this simple doubting of a dearly held principle of adaptation. So the young man substitutes honor, courage, fame, wealth, and now and then love, for the absence of pain and the presence of pleasure. Or now and then he substitutes evil—sadism, cruelty, criminality. In such an event we say that his adaptation went wrong. But how do we tell ourselves that a principle of adaptation is wrong?

In the literature of decision making today, it has become popular to talk of "levels of aspiration." The point is that a man does not always seek the best; instead, he seeks that which satisfies him, which meets his level of aspiration. But how shall a man know that his aspiration level is correct? What lessons does experience—or reason—teach him about his decision-making framework?

Perhaps the question so posed is the question of how a man can come to understand himself. Both the tragedy and the comedy of man lie in his self-deception: He can really believe fully and honestly that he understands his own psyche, and yet be as fooled as can the most imbecile fool. A man's misunderstanding of himself can be at least as deep as a manager's misunderstanding of his organization. The trouble is that we are often at a loss to find any guidance in our effort to find ourselves. Some seek religion, some psychoanalysis, some a friend, some quiet, some noise—and some, society.

The philosophical tradition of social sanctions cannot be ignored. It is the one great answer to the problem of self-reflection. Society will tell us whether our criteria of satisfaction are really satisfactory. The man bent on evil may feel satisfied with his choices, but society will not. If society cannot recondition him, it will eliminate him. It's that simple. "Law and order" must prevail, mustn't they?

The problem of self-reflection is too persistent—that's its trouble. If society is the answer for the individual, then what's the answer for society?

Who controls the controller? Who guards the custodian? Who imposes law on the law maker?

A worker receives his criteria of satisfactory work from his superior, and his superior from his superior, and so on to the top. And what of the "top?" The board of directors. And they? The stockholders. And they? The law makers. And they? The "people." And they?

The central problem of management today is internal control, in the broadest sense of the word, because internal control means instituting procedures to assure a satisfactory performance of the company. But what are the controls of internal control?

The founders of our nation were geniuses of organization. They saw that the only adequate answer to the problem of a free society was a system of "checks and balances": The people elect the law makers and executives, who freely appoint the courts, who control the people, the law makers, and the executives.

But how self-reflective is the U.S.A. today? Who tells the people that the national goals are satisfactory? Who tells the people that they no longer truly elect their representatives? Or that the courts are honest? Or that the executive has failed to be merely an executive?

How can man ever come to be self-reflective about his own goals? This seems to be the very deepest problem of the self-reflective mind. To gain some hint as to its nature, suppose we retrace our steps by means of a question that naturally occurs to a scientific mind. It is the question that demands of all questions that they be precisely put. Have we really been pursuing the same problem throughout this book?

Perhaps not. The problem of logic is a very direct one: How can a proposition talk about itself? The other problems—of measurement, of adaptive systems, of self, of society—seem to be different. They ask how a system can control itself. But each of these questions may entail quite different meanings, because the proper control of measurement may be describable in terms of statistical stability, whereas the proper control of society may not.

Nonetheless, there may be a hint in the distinction. The problem of logic is very direct. It arises because a proposition seemingly implies itself and yet implies its contradictory. It must therefore be false. But its negation does the same thing: It implies itself and its contradictory. The original proposition must therefore be true. Without trying at the present time to be any more precise, suppose we say that the logical paradox involves a *minimum loop.*

By the same score, we might then say that the successful outcome of the problem of self-reflection is to find a minimum loop that leads from x to x. This seems to have been the spirit that guided the intellectual efforts of Descartes and Spinoza in the seventeenth century. For Descartes, the problem was to find a proposition that leads directly to its own validity. No creation of the intellectual mind has ever been so direct as his, "I think, therefore I am." The one thing that no thinking mind can ever do is to obliterate its own thinking. I cannot doubt that I think without thinking about it. In the same way, Spinoza posits a human faculty of mind which he calls "intuition"; it is the faculty that guarantees knowledge. It has the supremely elegant ability to know—directly—that it knows.

It is the judgment of history that these great minds of the seventeenth century failed. The philosophical sceptics have pointed out that Descartes' class of undeniable propositions is empty, and that Spinoza's faculty of intuition—if it exists—is inoperative.

The opposite of the minimum loop is the maximum loop. The principle is fantastic. It says that self-reflection is possible only if one returns to the self after the longest possible journey. It is exemplified in the great myths of the heroes: Ulysses must go through every deep experience of human life before he can come to his resting point. In the great dramas of music: The simple Freude of the Ninth is only possible after the gigantic explorations of the first three movements.

The principle of the maximum loop was well expressed by the nineteenth-century scientists: The need to sweep into the model of Nature "all" that is relevant. No matter how small the disturber nor how minuscule his disturbance, he must eventually become a part of the scheme of Nature as we push on to the next decimal place. He, like the giants, will take his place in the scheme of things—or, as we say today, in the model.

The maximum-loop principle is based on a monistic philosophy: There is one world of interconnected entities, not many. The most distant galaxies and the most menial worker somehow have a connection.

The principle is also teleological. For the mind to know itself, it must also know the destiny of all minds as well as all matters. Indeed, the principle comes straight down to us from Plato, who taught its formulation in a clearly teleological style.

Perhaps I can capture both the obscurity and the spirit of the maximum loop by referring to three historical incidents, two quite ancient, one very recent. The last is a development made possible by the advent of the high-speed computer. Computers can be used to "simulate" various aspects and processes of reality. They can behave like people, or business firms, or fire-fighting equipment, or an air force. Could they simulate a scientific experimenter? Presumably, little ingenuity would be required to create a simulator that would develop hypotheses, make observations, run appropriate statistical tests of significance, write a paper, submit it to a journal, reply to the referee, and even read galleys. The number of accepted papers of such a simulator might easily qualify it for a tenure position within a very few years. But we would want to say that a simulator that generates hypotheses in so facile a manner is not an experimenter at all, because the next result an experimenter demands is as complete an understanding of the data as can be obtained: The loop that begins with one test and ends in the next must be maximal. To simulate an experimenter must require all that a discipline can offer.

The second incident is that point in history when Euclid was trying to prove a very important theorem of his *Elements,* and, failing to find the proof, postulated instead. At that point in time a minimum-loop logician would have said that Euclid's Parallel Postulate "implies itself." Afterward were two millennia of intellectual struggle to prove the postulate. Only by the time of Gauss, a century and a half ago, could it be said that the implications of the Parallel Postulate were getting clearer. Would it be perverting language to say that only then could we truly say that men understood what "implies itself" really means—only when all the fundamental implications and implicators had been laid before us by the historical struggle? A proposition can only be shown to imply itself when one can demonstrate all the fundamental implication links of the formal system that lead to it and away from it.

The last incident, already referred to, is all too well known. It occurs when Plato, simulating Socrates, suggests that the proper way to understand justice for the individual is via the route of political science, that is, justice for the state. He merely voiced the common sense of the ages: A man comes last of all to understanding himself—after he has come to understand all there is for him to understand.

These three illustrations capture so well the feeling of frustration that many systems scientists experience when they try to study the fundamental problems of sectors of our society. I can well remember my attempts to advise railroad managers. These were men who had come up through the ranks and clearly knew far more than I could ever hope to about the intricacies of railroad operations. They were correct in saying that what I could contribute would be naïve. They were wrong, however, in saying that a naïve system-science approach to railroads was useless. The approach provided another way of looking at a railroad—as a system, not as a physical instance of transportation. Since then, I have had the same experience with managers in health, law, education, defense, and production. They all want to know how an operations researcher in six months, or a year, or ten years, could ever hope to "solve" their problems. Of course, he can't, for he is no more of an expert than they are about the really fundamental problems. But he can provide a link of the maximum loop, a way to reflect, that no profession by itself can ever hope to provide.

"For a mind to understand itself, it must understand everything." But neither Plato, nor Leibniz, nor any subsequent philosopher has yet succeeded in giving the principle a precise and satisfactory form.

In the first place, can one take it seriously? Or ought one to do so? We cannot understand precisely even the smallest of organisms or organizations. How could we ever obtain a model of everything?

The intellectual opposition becomes clear. On the one side are those who are satisfied with being satisfied. They are the scientists who appeal to agreement, to precision, to esteem of one's peers. They wish to keep the problem small enough so it can be worked on. What comes after, or over and above, is a matter of common faith.

On the other side are those who are dissatisfied with satisfaction. They are the scientists who wonder why men study the problems they do, why they reach intellectual agreement, why esteem is a desirable outcome of research. They wish to make the problem large enough so the next problem that emerges will be a better one. They are faithless at heart. Or rather, they put their faith in the non-obvious rather than the obvious. In a way, their faith is deeply obscure.

A *unified science of management*—is it a matter of faith or of enterprise? A unified science of management conceals the self-reflective paradox. Science is an organized activity. Hence it operates according to some managerial principles. A unified science of management implies a management of science: a science of science, a self-reflective science.

The intellectually curious can at least go so far as to try to define the concept of a loop, and indeed have already started to do so. They may even begin to talk about the length of a loop. In this way they may begin to make clear what this part is talking about. But they will not thereby display the dangers of a self-reflective science. The danger is clear: If men begin to understand what they are trying to do, they may understand the worse as well as the better about themselves. Can they stand to understand?

science and god

Some eight decades ago Zarathustra announced the news that God was dead. This bit of philosophical arrogance on Nietzsche's part no doubt irritated the sensibilities of a Victorian world, much as Hedda Gabler's "unnecessary" suicide at the end of a harrowing last act evoked from Judge Black the priceless commentary: "People don't do such things!" Gods don't die. Or do they?

So far as the scientific world was concerned, Zarathustra's antics were irrelevant. The matter of God and His role in science had long since been settled: He has no role. Science had declared itself: Whether God exists, the manner in which He exists, and the attitude each person should have toward Him are problems each must decide within himself and are not the concern of science. The God of science had been given His notice a century before Nietzsche's *Zarathustra* was written. Empiricism and positivism, the philosophical spokesmen of science, phrased it thus: Empirical science can develop a sound theory of evidence without having to prove the existence of a deity. So few have questioned the validity of empiricism's analysis of the problem that it is difficult to believe that there *was* an earlier age of science that held just the opposite conviction. We have become so used to the concept of a personal God, that today it seems quite ridiculous to suggest for serious consideration a "science" of theology. I wonder with what astonishment those who apply science to decision making would greet a program of one of their societies that featured a session on "The Role of God in Optimization Theory." How would they react if there appeared a standard text in operations research devoting its first part to the proof of the existence of God and a discussion of His properties?

Yet some such procedure as this would have appeared the only reasonable way to write such a text to an operations researcher of seventeenth-century Europe. For that age and place, a scientist must come to grips with the problem of God's reality if he is to be a scientist at all. According to Leibniz, optimization without a concept of God is a dangerous and irresponsible piece of thinking.

It is not difficult to appreciate why the great minds of the seventeenth century felt this way. They pictured themselves to be embarking on a new intellectual enterprise in which reason was to become the supreme guide. For them, an issue that cannot be settled rationally cannot be settled at all. But this enterprise would be utterly futile unless one were assured that his rational convictions are in accordance with reality. One of the most beautiful pieces of intellectual deliberation is Descartes' *Meditations*, where he submits himself to the awful and ultimate question of all intellectual life: the possibility of a reality in which deception predominates.

It would seem utterly inappropriate to the seventeenth-century mind to speak of reason as many of us do today. For example, mention has already been made of the idea that a "rational" man must make his choices in compliance with what is called the *transitivity of preference*: "If A is preferred to B, and B to C, than A must be preferred to C." The advocates of this view of rationality are personally convinced that after a man has committed himself to preferring A to B and B to C, he could not possibly believe he preferred C to A, provided he understands the meanings of the terms. But to Descartes the whole method is suspect, because a rational man has to understand *why* he is convinced, and not merely *that* he is convinced. In our contemporary terms, he must construct a model of the world in which personal conviction is connected causally to truth: He must show that if he is convinced, then he is right. If it were possible to have a world in which man firmly believes what is not true in reality, no conviction has any weight in settling any issue: neither the convictions of sense nor the full agreement of all. The first problem of thinking minds, therefore, is to show that no such world of deception is possible. For Descartes, this can be done by showing that reality is designed by a God whose perfection guarantees that there is no fundamental deception. In contemporary terms, no conclusions about reality are warranted until we understand the basic structure of the whole system.

Most philosophers of science writing after Descartes, Leibniz, and Spinoza simply dropped the spirit of European rationalism. A scientist, they said, can become convinced that something is so by observing it. He doesn't have to concern himself with the relationship between conviction and reality, because all that matters is his observations, and he knows he has these. If there is any reality beside what lies in the scientist's observational reports, it has no relevance for science. A subtle Descartes could still have asked how the scientist knows he observes, but this would have been considered an arrogant, nonsensical question that is best ignored.

Reason, of course, suffered its inevitable fate in this intellectual war. For Descartes it was the supreme source of all evidence; for science today it simply puts observation in an orderly array. For Leibniz, the reason of God establishes the ultimate purpose and destiny of man and his environment; for today's science, reality has no purpose or destiny other than the little that observation tells us.

Thus reason became the subject matter of logic and logic became the inventor of languages. Since languages are conventions, reason becomes the convenient way to discuss and infer. Reason does the necessary but menial work of science, and we are all in a hurry to get its task onto computers so that we won't have to think about it any more.

Of course, there were a few diehards in this long process of killing off the Age of Reason and its God. There was Hegel, who suggested a dialectical teleology; the end point of the process of reality is an Absolute Mind. But Marx showed that it was far more significant to use the dialectic method to describe a sociological, materialist process without a God.

Then there were those quaint folk called *normative economists,* who found in the concept of reason an excellent method of prescribing choices. Empirical sociology can describe the choices men make; can economics prescribe the choices they ought to make? The answer is "yes," provided one can construct an idealized model of free choice when the outcomes are known. So normative economists created economic man, who does not exist, but who is the prototype of all prescriptions. But this century has been doing its best to kill off even this bit of nineteenth-century fantasy. Economic man could scan all alternatives. But is it wise to scan all alternatives when making plans? Perhaps the time and cost of such scanning are disastrously large. Hence economic man becomes adaptive man, and adaptive man behaves "nonrationally," according to classical ideas. For economic man, information was free. But information, today, is not free. Hence, a manager today must make "nonrational" choices to remain "economical."

One may struggle to save reason by arguing that if search and other information costs are incorporated into the model, one can establish rational criteria of behavior. But all of us know that this is a pitiful way to "save" the concept of reason. All these models simply say that *if* the manager is trying to maximize long-range profits, he ought rationally to do so-and-so. Reason in this context is merely the servant of the policy maker. It is not permitted to say anything about the basic value assumptions. For example, is it rational to maximize long-range profits? It is not appropriate to ask this question.

Nowhere has reason suffered such an ignominious fate as in psychology. We are told that men have nonrational impulses that "ought" to be obeyed. As we have seen, C. G. Jung sees nothing odd in dividing the psyche into functions, and relegating rationality to thinking and feeling; the other "nonrational" functions (sensation and intuition) also play their role in the fully developed individual.

Hence, our intellectuals today are content to work with Godless models of reality and/or reasonless theories of optimization. God is an unnecessary concept, reason is a secondary concept.

The opposite viewpoint, as we have seen, calls for a revival of the Age of Reason, because thereby some of the most troublesome problems of reflection would receive legitimate answers. The question "Why are your basic values correct?" is self-reflective and is un-answerable in empiricist philosophy. But this is a question of critical importance in a rational approach to social design. For example, how can we rationally solve labor-management problems? We can't re-gard labor-and-management as a single group with one clearcut ob-jective. We have to determine a "reasonable" way to compromise. A reasonable compromise must be based on reasonable objectives; that is, reason must be able to tell us which objectives are proper ones. This is why so-called game theory is not an adequate rational solution of serious conflict problems. Game theory does not question the leg-itimacy of the goals of the players; instead it develops very ingenious and often rigorous "fair-play" strategies by assuming that the goals of the players are *given* and thus unreflectively accepted.

If one man is "playing" to save the life of his family, and the other is playing to make a dollar, game theory would find both to be fair if they played according to rules. The kind of rationality that the seventeenth century called for would be one in which goals can be judged rationally, and would not be derivations of the selfish pur-poses of players of games. If we could be as confident as Descartes or Spinoza were about the meaning of reason, we would proceed to de-velop optimization models for social conflict, for urban planning, for international negotiation, in which "compromise" means *in accor-dance with rational goals*. We would say, in our negotiations with Soviet Russia, "You are unreasonable," and mean by this something more than "You don't agree with us." However, to many it will seem futile to ascribe rationality to goals, unless the goals are regarded as intermediate means to further ends. Since they believe that reason fundamentally deals with "if, then" kind of thinking, it can never tell us what is absolutely right, but only what is right given certain as-sumptions. Somewhat irrationally, they have never considered that reason might have a far more general meaning.

What are the prospects then for a Renaissance of Reason? At first glance, many serious thinkers will hope that they aren't very good. Such an amount of nonsense or downright political evil is propagated under the name of reason, that to suggest a Renaissance of Reason seems to suggest opening the gates to intellectual charlatans. Reason is so often used as the justification of the unjustifiable. Men want to prove to other men that the universe is run the way they think it is, and they justify their convictions by an appeal to reason. The idea seems to be that reason is direct and simple, and that reasonableness is easy to come by. Therefore, the reasonable fools of today can prove to their simple satisfaction that communism is dangerous to man, that communism is the salvation of man; that the individual is all-important, that society is all-important; that science and technology are the greatest threats of all time to mankind, that they are man's chief blessing.

The objection to all these fallacious claims about reason is not an objection to elevating reason to a primary position in our thinking, but rather an objection to regarding reason as simple. This was the error of the seventeenth-century philosophers, who held that the proof of God's existence must be simple. They agreed that it was no simple matter to find this simple proof, but they also believed that the proof once found must appear simple to all reasonable men.

Today, we begin to suspect that reason is not a simple concept at all. More precisely, we suspect that it is an expanding concept, so that its nature is not built out of the obvious and simple ingredients of common sense. It is a mistake to assume that the basic principles of rational behavior must be obvious and clear to all. It is a mistake to assume that a rational policy can be reduced to a set of simple precepts that everyone will recognize to be valid.

If there is to be another Age of Reason, it must be constructed along lines quite different from its predecessor. The seventeenth century built the universe from simple components; our century cannot. What is demanded is a basis for judgment that satisfies the scientific criteria of objectivity and at the same time goes far enough to say something significant about the universe.

In place of the term *God*, the term that typifies our gropings for a twentieth-century rationalism is *system*. A system is rational: It explains, it unifies, it does all the things for its components that Spinoza's and Leibniz's God did for theirs. People differentiate between societies and mankind. Mankind is the largest system of all societies. People differentiate between pure and basic research. Science is the largest system of all research. People differentiate between the business firm and its social setting. Industrial society is the largest system of all business firms and their environments.

The cautious, pure empiricist finds all this talk about systems to be ridiculous and overworked. How do we know there is such a thing as mankind, or science, or society? For that matter, how do we prove that there is such a thing as an organization? Or a group mind? If the only things we know are what we see, we cannot prove that organizations and group minds "exist." To an empiricist, our imagination may roam as freely as it pleases, but when the hand is called it's only the cards that show that count. So the empiricist lives in a strange world of intervening variables, subjective probabilities and distasteful judgments, which are the nonexistent ghosts of his haunted house. Indeed, he lives in no world at all, since "worlds" don't "exist."

Ross Ashby has put the intellectual battle quite clearly: "Science has, of course, long been interested in the living organism; but for two hundred years, it has tried primarily to find, within the organism, whatever is *simple* . . . .

"Thus, until recently the strategy of science has been largely that of analysis. The units have been found, their properties studied, and then, somewhat as an after-thought, some attempt has been made to study them in combined action. But this study of synthesis has often made little progress and does not usually occupy a prominent place in scientific knowledge."[1]

From the point of view of synthesis, rather than analysis, the so-called simple component, so clear to the heart of the empiricist, is not simple at all. It is a component only because someone has had the imagination to construct the system of which it is a part; it is highly complicated because to show in what way it is a com-

[1]W. Ross Ashby, "General Systems Theory as a New Discipline," *General Systems*, Vol. 3, 1958, p. 1.

ponent at all is a long and tedious task. The issue is not whether systems exist; the issue is whether a component exists. The greatest unsolved problem of our science is whether my observations have any existence at all. They exist only if they are components of a larger system.

Such talk reminds us very much of Descartes, who could see no way to proceed until he had seen the most general way. He was convinced that $2 + 2 = 4$, and this was surely a unit of his clear thinking. But he could not accept his conviction until he had seen that $2 + 2 = 4$ is a component of a system large enough to guarantee its validity.

In the early days of operations research, its spokesmen often tried to explain the nature of their discipline by saying that operations research "looks at the whole system" or the whole organization. Of course they were often vague as to how this was done. The spirit of their claim was clear, however. They meant that to concentrate on a part and neglect the purpose of the whole is to invite disaster in recommending changes in organizational operations. The spirit is the same as that of Leibniz, who wanted scientists to have regard for the final purpose of the whole universe.

But is it fair to make this comparison? Is it fair, for example, to say that the General Systems Society is science's call for a rationalist religion? Is it correct to say that professors of operations research who tell their students to "look at the whole system" are telling them to prove God's existence first before they embark on the study of the firm?

The answer, of course, may well be an emphatic "No!" Whole Systems and General Systems people may be more modest. They may only mean "understand enough to get on with the problem." But as we move in our studies from production to the firm, from the firm to the city, from the city to the state, the state to the nation, the nation to the internation, the "enough" gets to be very large indeed.

Even so, where is God in all this grasping for the whole? Ashby, at least, is not asking us to construct an ideal system. He believes that complexity is the order of Nature as She is, not as She ought to be. The general systems he discusses are therefore the systems that actually occur in biological entities, in the stellar world, in human organizations.

But operations research does seek to reconstruct the world. Its "whole system" is a better system than the actual. Hence its prescription to study the whole system is a prescription to understand the better system, and eventually the best system.

Each more comprehensive "best" system supplies the justification of optimality and the stability of its subsystems. The seventeenth-century model of system stability asserted that there must be a maximal optimal system that guarantees the stability of all systems, including itself. It was the ultimate Guarantor Of Decisions.[2] At the risk of confusion, and for the sake of maintaining the historical reference of this chapter, let us call the maximal system God—trying to recognize that *this* God is a concept of the science of decision making.

Does the best system, or God, so defined, really exist? If we could prove that it does, we would indeed be thinking again in the spirit of an Age of Reason. Now we do insist that the whole systems we contemplate be realizable, in the sense that pathways to them be real possibilities. Hence, we could say that the whole systems we model exist because of our faith in the rationality of man. If men come to reason clearly, then better systems will exist.

But so moderate a concession to reason won't do. It loses the whole spirit of the Age of Reason simply to say that reason depends on faith, for then faith is no longer reasonable. We can't say, "We *hope* that men will adopt our realizable systems, but our hope has no reasonable grounds."

No, the spirit of the whole-system concept demands a much more radical position, far less convincing on common-sense grounds. The whole systems we prescribe must be based on sound prediction and not faith alone. We must hold that men will adopt them because they are in the proper images of man. If men hesitate to accept our recommendations because they are suspicious by nature, or arrogant, or anxiety-ridden, then our recommendations are not rational.

[2]That is, G.O.D. Many thanks are due to the late Wroe Alderson for this way of putting things. In a private letter he suggested "Guardian of our Destiny."

They have failed to capture the rationality that underlies man's universe.

So we could end by saying that operations research is at the forefront in the movement toward a new Age of Reason. This age will regard science and society as whole systems; it will seek the whole system that is the optimal system. It will therefore bring back the concept of God as a necessary concept of all research.

We could say all this and be willing to face the mighty outcry of anguish of the empirical purist. We could say to him that his research, no matter how elegant and profound, is the ashes of a meaningless intellectual fire unless our system survives in such a manner that it also develops, that is, improves.

We could say all this were it not for the same awful suspicion that haunts the pages of Descartes' *Meditations*: The whole system that is man may be evil. In our modern-day language, the whole system that is man may be completely unstable. The destiny that man will choose may be the point of a sardonic joke: Let the poor fools become serious about their living to prove in the end that living in any form is an evil. The whole system may have built into it the necessary ingredients of its own destruction.

This is our intellectual problem today: To show that the realizable and to-be-realized pathways of systems change are those of systems development. To have the imagination to construct a world view that is at one time realizable, to-be-realized, and best. To show, by very hard work, that it may be possible after all to create a science that deserves a God.

the heroism of
applied science

In these days when men have come to reflect quite seriously about the growth of research and development, we hear a great deal of debate about the proper allocation of our scarce intellectual resources. One question of considerable interest to all of us is the debate about the proper allocation of effort to pure and applied research.

In this debate much has been said in praise of pure science. Sometimes the praise is for the purity itself: It is science carried out with no objective other than the pursuit of truth. But sometimes the praise is for the impurity itself: Look at all the blessings that flow from pure research! Hydraulic people even talk as though pure research pumps into a reservoir from which applied research gets its water, and, eagerly pushing their analogy on, they say there is danger that the reservoir will dry up or that the U.S.A. reservoir is lower than the U.S.S.R. reservoir, and so on. There is far less talk about the danger of too little applied research, but the analogy hints that if people don't use the reservoir it may overflow and drown us all.

There is something very insidious about this hydraulic analogy over and above its implication that science is all wet. For one thing, the analogy places applied science in a particular relationship to basic science: Applied science "draws" from basic science, not vice versa. Furthermore, applied science may rob basic science of its resources.

Now it seems to me that there are two very different ways of thinking about applied science. One way is to make the applied scientist a searcher; he searches for problems that he believes can feasibly be solved by applying the results of science; he isn't interested in why the problem arose, or whose problem it is, so long as the problem can be stated precisely and is amenable to scientific attack. The other way is to regard the applied scientist as someone who is interested in improving the real world; he is a missionary bent on doing good; he's very interested in how the problem arose, and judges the importance of the problem by its relevance to improvement.

The first kind of applied scientist is like the pure scientist. They are both pure because they can shut off most of reality and just look at a piece of it—objectively, dispassionately, precisely. In the management sciences, a transport problem becomes a "linear programming problem," *given* sufficient information about costs and requirements. The word *given* is important here, for it implies that the pure applied scientist has every right to expect that information of various types will be available, and if it is not available, he turns his attention elsewhere.

Thus the purity of pure science lies in its isolation; it creates a small system that it can work on, and expects that various gifts it calls *data* can be obtained. It is a marvelous creation of the human intellect, sometimes beautiful to behold and understand—but all in all it is not very heroic.

The real hero is the applied scientist who inquires in order to improve systems. He takes upon himself the hopeless task of all those who aspire to do good in the world. It's a tragic aspiration, really.

Why is doing good so heroic an enterprise? Simply because one must take on the whole world as an antagonist as well as ally. Suppose the hero wishes to improve a supply system of an army. At first blush his ambition has none of the heroic quality of a Jason in search of a Golden Fleece, or a Washington preserving starving troops.

But supply systems are not isolated pieces of an army, nor are armies isolated pieces of a government, nor governments isolated pieces of society. If someone sets about improving supply systems, he must ask himself what "improvement" really means. Inevitably he will have to ask whether the system that embeds the supply system is any good in the first place, because to improve that which is fundamentally bad is to create evil, not good. It might be fascinating from the pure science point of view to design a supply system for the largest gang in Chicago, but someone bent on "improving" the system would have to decide how to make it maximally ineffective if he felt that gangsterism had no place in society.

Every heroic applied scientist working for the military has taken on the tremendous moral burden of deciding whether there should be a Department of Defense of the type we now have, a system used both for the defense of democracy and the destruction of humans. He must decide on such matters *as* an applied scientist—and not merely as a citizen—because it is a problem of his applied science to determine whether improvement is possible. Lurking behind every decision he makes is the awful speculation that the world would be better off without the system for which he works.

No wonder applied scientists avoid the heroic and turn back to the pure. They find far greater security and comfort in isolating themselves from the heroic mood. Perhaps they simply adopt a master-slave attitude, and recognize that they work for some organization that supports them. They trust the managers and the managers trust them. They trust that the managers will determine policy and administration along socially healthy lines, and the managers trust that the scientists will solve the subproblems of the system adequately. Theirs not to question why this mutual trust is morally sound! Now of course all men should trust each other as long as men are trustworthy. But blind loyalty is just that—blind. To put blind trust in another is not to see him as he is; indeed, it is not even to respect him for what he is.

No, the heroic applied scientist cannot find solace in the mood of mutual trust, unless he can see the basis on which trust is to be built. He must struggle to understand why he should trust the policy makers.

It is true that these days—and especially in Washington, D.C.—
we hear a great deal about separating the scientist and the politician.
The scientist is supposed to concern himself with matters of science—
and hence he is not supposed to tell the decision maker what to do.
He is supposed to give advice when it is called for, and when he is
equipped to do so. This kind of separation of scientist and politician—if not downright cowardly—is certainly not heroic. How can
one "give advice" to a man who must make the terrifying decisions
without taking on the moral burden of the whole issue? Even if the
scientist does not make the decision—or does not tell the manager
how to make it—nevertheless he, the scientist, does decide to advise.
If he advises a man who is not worthy, then he the scientist is not
worthy either; both are mutually untrustworthy.

We also hear a great deal about the need to use the knowledge
we have—to "spin off" technology to potential users. The difference
between where we are and where we might be if we applied our
science is appalling. Men continue to use antiquated techniques
long beyond their technological obsolescence. Why? Is it because
managers are irrational or just plain stupid? Or is it because those
who admire the shiny newness of a technological advance ignore
the older and deeper values of the human race?

In recent years at Berkeley an attempt has been made to simulate the life of an applied scientist in the laboratory. A group of
subjects is asked to run a small business firm, which has a "small"
problem to solve. Carefully prepared and planted in the group is
a "stooge" who knows the solution to the problem. Here is technological spin-off in its purest form. All the stooge has to do is convince his fellow subjects that truth is truth. But he usually fails—
miserably. Why? Because the other subjects somehow don't recognize him for the wise man he is; because they are too busy, because
they are indifferent, because they already know their jobs very well.
I was about to say "because they are human." After all, our stooge
is a very arrogant fellow. He knows how to maximize profits by a
fully automated plan. Why shouldn't the rest of his fellow men
recognize his science and apply it? Well, at least because his
"solution" is inhuman.

There isn't one aspect of modern technology that doesn't impinge on the human spirit, often in a thoroughly undignified manner. Freeways are wonderful technological inventions, but they have a way of making us all into morons as we line up, one behind the other, belts about our fat bellies, sitting there eyes forward, waiting for the privilege to push our right foot forward one-eighth of an inch. Freeways imprison the free spirit of the homeward-bound pigeons.

Many a management scientist would like to improve the system for which he works, and many plan to do this by means of automation. Will their so-called solutions also be inhuman?

There is a middle-ground answer to this question and to all that is implied in its tragic mood. It is the so-called adaptive answer that is neither pure nor heroic. It says that man can learn, but his learning curve does not necessarily increase concerning all aspects of his nature. We push forward along one line—for example, rationalizing a manufacturing system—and our learning curve goes up with respect to economy. But the new system disrupts the lives of some of the system inhabitants; our learning curve goes down with respect to human dignity. We therefore consider the dignity problem and develop, say, a retraining program to save the lives of the displaced people; the learning curve goes up with respect to human dignity. But the retraining program siphons off teaching talent from other areas; the learning curve goes down with respect to educational economy. It's as though we were struggling to push up a large flexible roof, but each time we exert an effort in one place, the roof sinks in another.

According to the adaptive viewpoint, we can learn from an overall point of view. Over time, the whole flexible roof rises. Adherents to this viewpoint don't have very much evidence for their belief. They like to point to the parts of the roof that have soared: medical care, transportation, communication, etc. They like to ignore the parts that have sagged: international security, technological ugliness, a humanist depression. But in any event, the analogy of the roof suggests a safe approach to the problem of applied science, namely, to seek problems broad enough in scope yet feasible in solution, where

a maximum net improvement will occur. Indeed, in any organization there appear to be a whole host of little irrationalities that can
be cleared up without noticeably changing the rest of the organization. If someone is using a quill pen, you can suggest he use a ball
point without having the roof fall in. This may be so, but the trouble
is the same one mentioned earlier: The man who uses the quill may
be signing death warrants of innocent people. Better, perhaps, that
he use an inadequate instrument so that occasionally the execu-
tioner can't decipher the name.

The analogy of the roof thus breaks down, as does the whole
adaptive position. Of course, if we could see the whole structure we
were trying to elevate, then our fears might be removed. But since
we are working in a given section, we may be behaving ridiculously,
if not dangerously. We may be engaged in making an ineffective
part become efficiently ineffective.

I well realize that people are fond of saying that the scientist
cannot possibly cope with all aspects of the problem that the decision
makers must face, and that this is what relegates the scientist to
an advisory role. But as an earlier chapter has argued, there seems
to be no sound basis for believing in the existence of a magic that
enables our President, our Congress, our agency managers, our corporation managers, to sift through all the critical aspects of a problem and come up with an action that has overall effectiveness.
For magic it is, from the viewpoint of the pure scientist. It is magic
that cannot be articulated except in the mumbo jumbo of *Business
Reviews*: It is horse sense, common sense, know-how, leadership, insight. The only way we know this magic is through observing success. It's much as though we were all assigned numbers at random
and selected as our leaders the ones who received the highest scores.
The heroic applied scientist takes upon himself the awful burden
of doubt; he doubts, for example, that any man is magically endowed
with the powers to understand the whole system. He demands of
himself some way of looking at reality that will guarantee that his
advice is good and not evil.

In a recent article, David Hertz suggests that management
scientists and operations researchers have studied only the trivial

problems of management; they have been relegated to housekeeping problems, not house construction problems. This is perhaps why operations research has attracted so many pure-science types, and why its most recognized contributions have been models and algorithms. We will be able to rationalize almost anything in a while, including the operations of the Devil as well as of God. This is both a marvelous development and a frightening one—marvelous because we can know that an operation will function according to optimal rules, frightening because it may be optimally decadent.

In my youth I studied scientific method—and learned all about experimental design, maximum likelihood, orthogonal fits and their chi-squares. With this in hand, I went out to convert the heathen physicist and chemist. "Throw away your French rules," I said, "and do things in a fitting manner!" Scientific method, I thought, was the method of logic adapted to observation and thought. And this method so patiently developed over the ages seems still to be the appropriate method of pure science. But for the applied scientist of the heroic type, the method is sadly lacking, because by its very nature it draws attention away from the whole system with its vagueness and enormous uncertainties, and concentrates on the precise and specific.

For the applied scientist, scientific method must include a philosophy of the whole system, however vague, however inadequate, however difficult to defend. It is what the Germans call a *Weltanschauung*, a perception of what reality is like. It becomes an integral part of the applied scientist's behavior. This, above all, is why the applied scientist is not merely applying the results of pure research; he is also applying his Weltanschauung.

Now in some sense, the pure scientist and the adaptive scientist do have a Weltanschauung. The pure scientist believes he can discover truth in a piece of reality without disturbing the whole, and the adaptive scientist believes he can raise the roof here without collapsing it elsewhere. But their Weltanschauungen are naïve at best; their vision is myopic. The more heroic applied scientist tries to bear the burden of the enormous risk and vagueness of his Weltanschauung. His role, in true heroic fashion, is tragic: He must act, but he cannot ever know that his actions are good. His role is also comic: His actions have a humorous side that all will recognize. Being human, he is reluctant to become heroic. Like the sergeant in the *Pirates of Penzance* when the maidens so fervently urge the heroes on to glory and the grave:

> We observe too great a stress on the risks that on us press,
> And of reference a lack to our chance of coming back.

But this swing between the tragic and the comic is the basis of the human spirit; the applied scientist is—or struggles to be—both a humanist and a scientist. For him science is an art, an ethic, a comedy, and tragedy. The mood is well put by the poet:

> In my craft or sullen art
> Exercised in the still night
> When only the moon rages
> And the lovers lie abed
> With all their griefs in their arms,
> I labour by singing light
> Not for ambition or bread
> Or the strut and trade of charms
> On the ivory stages
> But for the common wages
> Of their most secret heart.
>
> Not for the proud man apart
> From the raging moon I write
> On these spindrift pages
> Nor for the towering dead
> With their nightingales and psalms
> But for the lovers, their arms
> Round the grief of the ages,
> Who pay no praise or wages
> Nor heed my craft or art.

the humor
of science

Anyone who from the title expects some relaxation in a good-humored essay will be disappointed. Talking about humor is a deadly serious matter, especially when a philosopher does it. Philosophers love to generalize, but humor is always specific if not unique. Philosophers love to categorize, but humor is always tricky and loves to "punish" the categorizer.

If I were to adopt the attitude of an expert, how dully I'd begin by defining humor, and then I'd go on to declare why it is important for science. But I am not writing as an expert on the subject of humor, as you will soon realize. Compared with the expert, I feel very much like the character in an old rabbi story. Only instead of the rabbi, I'll choose some very famous management scientist, Professor Charnzig, say. The professor was on a lecture tour, accompanied by a young and ambitious chauffeur. Near the end of the tour the chauffeur remarked how marvelous it must be to stand up and give all those lectures and hear all the applause and praise. "Oh, I don't know," said Charnzig immodestly, "it's really quite a bore." But the chauffeur insisted, until Charnzig said, "Well, see here; no one knows me at the next college, why don't you read the lecture? I'll even help you pronounce the difficult words." Thus it came about that the chauffeur read the lecture so bashfully titled "A Few Fundamental Contributions to Generalized Network Flows." Then came the question period, and an eager assistant professor arose from the rear and said, "Professor, we've been waiting a long while to ask you an important question: How do you compare out-of-kilter with the simplex method in semi-chance constrained networks?" The chauffeur, without a pause, replied, "I can't imagine why you'd ask such a simple question here. Why, it's the kind of thing my youngster has already mastered in his fifth-grade mathematics, and just to prove it, I'm going to ask my chauffeur to give you the answer!"

If you laughed at all, that's your last. The rest, as I said, is deadly serious. I began my research into the humor of science because I have long felt the essential incompleteness of our modern concept of science. The humanists are right in their claim that science—as it is described by scientists themselves—is a kind of inhuman monster. One rather successful young scientist I know likes to differentiate between hard and soft science; presumably, hard science means the inhuman beast who tries to gobble up reality by its monstrously mathematically precise teeth and digest it in its huge programmed belly which can accommodate a million variables. Soft science, I suppose, is soft in the head.

Hard science is precise, rigorous, objective; it is also humorless, ugly, and at best amoral. It goes around creating "knowledge about the world," and it doesn't care who uses the knowledge, or why. This is not quite accurate, of course. When he's not hard at work, the hard scientist is usually a very nice fellow, just like the felon:

> When a scientist's not engaged in his employment
> Or maturing his felonious little plans,
> His capacity for innocent enjoyment
> Is just as great as any honest man's.
>
> Our feelings we with difficulty smother
> When scientific method's to be done.
> Ah, take one consideration with another,
> A scientist's lot is not a happy one.

Actually, the hard scientist does have a kind of pawky humor that few except people of his kind can appreciate. For example, there is an hilarious joke going about among the better mathematicians: If you write "lion" on a piece of paper, then be sure that—before applying the inverse operator—you put the piece of paper in a cage! If you laugh, you're identified as being either (a) hard, (b) nervous, or (c) asleep. That last remark is also typical of hard-science humor of a so-called logical kind.

The hard scientist also appreciates beauty and can become morally indignant. He's really quite human, once you get to know him. But he would insist that humor, beauty, and morality have nothing to do with being a scientist; at best, humor, beauty, and morality are by-products of the scientific endeavor.

I can't help wondering why this is so, and further, if it is so, whether it makes science incomplete—or even monstrous. Down the ages, reflective man has always said that for a man to become mature he must learn to see himself as he really is. And humor has a great deal to do with this ability to see yourself as you really are. Because you are ridiculous. Indeed, this follows from the well-known conjugation of the irregular verb "to be funny":

> I am witty.
> You are ridiculous.
> He is a boor.

What are we like when we are trying to be scientists? I recall one of the many hilarious experiments of one of my psychologist friends. (I'm convinced that the real test of the validity of any of his hypotheses is whether it makes you laugh.) In this very successful experiment, subjects were supposed to identify a code that they were led to think was written into a set of what were really randomly smeared slides. Each slide was to be identified as belonging—or not belonging—to a particular class. One group was reinforced, and were told after most of their guesses that they were right—very smart and right. The other group was told that they were almost always wrong—stupidly wrong. Not surprisingly, the first group developed some rather elaborate hypotheses; you know, "whenever there is a blue swirl in the upper lefthand corner and two dots at the bottom, it's an X, unless the background is ochre-colored, in which case it's a Y."

Then came the punch line of the experimental joke. A training school was established in which those who thought they had mastered the code trained the unsuccessful ones to read the slides. What a school! The students refused to recognize blue swirls, dots, or ochre colors, even when they were obvious to the "teachers." The real kickback came when the experimenters debriefed the subjects, because many a reinforced subject refused to believe that the slides were random smears, and was quite prepared to train the experimenters!

Experiments like these are getting a little closer to a malicious kind of scientific humor. They make the serious scientist objectively seeking to verify or refute his hypotheses look somewhat ridiculous and a little more human. The experiments described in the last chapter that are being run at Berkeley have much the same flavor with respect to management scientists. There are five subjects very seriously engaged in running a small business firm, with the apparent objective of maximizing profits. Then one of the subjects—our stooge—suddenly plays the role of a hard scientist. He "discovers" that the underlying model of the firm's operations is a deterministic linear price-quantity, economic-lot-size model, and esentially involves minimizing a nine-variable function subject to some constraints. He develops the algorithm and seriously presents it to the other four—who just as seriously are apt to ignore the correct solution entirely. They are too busy to study the analysis, or have been in their jobs too long to have to listen to some inexperienced person trying to tell them what to do. In a further attempt to draw out the humor, subjects were told that there were two other firms in their industry, call them Y and Z, and that the industry publishes a trade magazine. Both Y and Z were simulated, Y being a kind of aggregation of many other groups, and Z being "optimal"—that is, Z uses the optimal solution. In the trade magazine, each company publishes articles telling "how we set prices in the Y Company" or "how we schedule production in the Z Company." The subjects submit articles, and the articles from the other two companies are simulated. Actually, Y's articles sound very much like some that appear in management magazines; you know, "In the Y Company, we set prices by paying due regard to inventory and demand," which says nothing but is awfully easy to read. In the journal are printed all the decisions of the three companies and their financial statements. Z, the optimal, does very well, but its hard-science articles are not read by the members of X; instead our subjects read Y, and decide that the thing to do is to beat Y. Z is too serious, while Y is friendly and breezy. All this tells us a lot about the learning process in an organization, but perhaps it's also a humorous way to look at people who are very serious. The joke may be on the stooge, or ourselves.

Now to turn academic and start defining some terms. The needed term is *apperception*. Perception means looking at something in a meaningful—that is, a purposive—way. Apperception means the act of looking at the same thing in two quite different ways. Apperception happens to us all the time. We watch a cat at play. All of a sudden, it's not a cat but a dancer, creating a marvelous pattern of furry motion. We watch a mathematician earnestly struggling to solve a set of equations. All of a sudden, he's not a mathematician but an artist carefully placing strings of symbols together in a marvelous mosaic. A hobo is a cheap, downgraded, dirty form of humanity; Charlie Chaplin lets us apperceive him to be subtle, sensitive, and pathetically comical.

Of course I'll want to say that humor is a kind of apperception, but since I've just introduced a brand new term, let me play with it awhile. You can try your hand, too. You can apperceive me as a dull wit struggling to articulate the trivial—or a frustrated soft scientist, and so on.

Rational thinking is something all scientists admire. It goes ahead in a direct way from established premises to conclusions— and once the conclusion is reached, that's it! So, let's agree on the premises of human living, and let's carefully deduce the consequences of our agreed-upon premises, and that's that. How can a world filled with rational men of good will do the stupid things it does? All we need to do is bring people together and get them to agree on the fundamental principles of international life, and reason will tell us the rest.

Why doesn't this scheme work? Because there's no apperception. In such a scheme, no one has tried to apperceive assumption-making people deducing consequences. What are they like? They're like a lot of ants scurrying around grabbing up the crumbs and laying them by in an orderly fashion. They're like a bunch of accountants figuring out debits and credits. They lack sensibility—they are dull, monotonous. They are marvelous artists playing with symbols—they are silly.

Of course, the hard scientist should now get his licks. He loves to watch the vital, energetic manager who works 18 hours a day, seriously discussing, deliberating, and then making decisions in his determined style. What is this marvelous genius of the managerial age—this man of "know-how" who has built our great industrial empire? Why, simply a random device. And a most ridiculously expensive one to boot. When we simulate him, we apperceive that his so-called decisions could be thought of as the output of randomly connected pieces of information that float around in his memory box. One rather successful management scientist, who is admired by many a manager, in private often voices the opinion that there is no such thing as a decision. This is an hilarious joke—all these fine, earnest, important, powerful managers who pay him so handsomely and pay themselves more, but who never decide anything!

Apperception is something more than perceiving in multiple ways. It also connotes a mood. That is, as our way of seeing the world shifts from X to Y, our mood does as well. Satire is an excellent example. The opening sentence of one of a San Francisco satirist's daily columns was, "Now that President Johnson has sent 20,000 Marines to overcome 50 Communists of the Dominican·Republic. . . ." The apperception occurs if you happen to approve of Johnson's policy. Your mood shifts from serious hope to the sublimely ridiculous.

Our human moods are many, and indeed in earlier medicine were identified with the humors—the melancholic, phlegmatic, sanguine, and choleric. These labels of human temperament provide a typology of the moods of apperception. When we apperceive that the world is going to the dogs, our mood is melancholic; our image may be that men are seeking an atom-blasted earth, or that men are bent on evil, or whatever. When we apperceive that the world is an evolutionary process, our mood may be sanguine; our image may be biological, hierarchical, divine. When we apperceive that the world is an unfair game, our mood may be choleric; our image one of wolves or werewolves. When we listen long to speeches and observe them in a detached manner, our mood may be phlegmatic; our image a world of noise.

And finally, there is that spirit-freeing mood called the humorous. Its blessed quality is that it puts no further demands on the human spirit. The melancholic, the sanguine, the choleric, the phlegmatic all have their "therefores." But humor never does. It preaches no lesson, it insists on nothing whatever. If the spirit soars, no strings are attached.

The less apperceptive among you will long ago have asked what the point of this chapter can be. What am I trying to say—if anything? This is the sort of question we all ask when we are being intent on something. If we were a bit more apperceptive, we'd see that the point is one of our making, not someone else's.

In any event, I have a point to be made. Indeed, I can seriously propose a principle of scientific method at least as compelling as any to be found in the logic of hypothesis testing. The principle is: Thou shalt apperceive. Or, if you can't see a purposive activity in two very different ways with different moods, you have failed to formulate the problem.

Why should this be a principle of scientific method for science? Rather than apply it at first to science as a whole, suppose I talk about management science. My reasons for applying the principle to management science are based on a whole set of reasonings— ramblings of thought of someone who has been curious about this process we call management science and how it relates to the world of reality. The management scientist is not a pure scientist, that is, he does not spend his days objectively observing and calculating as the so-called pure scientist does. The pure scientist is phlegmatic; he is detached from the world he observes, and almost never does he sweep himself into the world of reality. He is not apperceptive. But the applied scientist—which the management scientist is—must learn to include himself in the world of reality. He can act like the pure scientist up to a point. He constructs models, makes observations, maximizes objective functions, all in a phlegmatic mood. But now comes the point of trying to change reality—to improve it. What arrogance! Now he is no longer phlegmatic. He must look at the whole world. But with a mixture of moods. If he turns sanguine, he sees himself and his recommendations as potentially doing good in the world. If he turns choleric, he sees himself as battling all the stupidity and dishonesty of men. If he turns melancholic, he sees the whole world as going down to inevitable destruction. A most marvelous mood combines the sanguine and the melancholic. (This is possible because, you know, emotions don't know anything about the law of contradiction.) This combination gives the heroic mood of the preceding chapter; it combines the aspirations of a do-gooder with the tragic mood that the world is too big and too powerful for us mortals to cope with. Pure science is phlegmatic and often sanguine; applied science is heroic as well.

To leave off being phlegmatic is to become more human; it is also to become closer to the real world of human change. The management scientist is not above or apart from the world he seeks to change. He can perceive himself as a trusted expert, of course, and when he does he is phlegmatic and sanguine. But he should also perceive himself as hopelessly lost in confusion about the realities of management, and when he does he may become melancholic.

But most of all he needs to perceive how ridiculous he really is. Now there is no technique of doing this, so that the principle is not a technical one; humor knows no technique. But it is a sound principle for all those who want to be management scientists, that is, human as well as scientific. The human person can apperceive in many ways with many moods—and especially the humorous.

And built into all this talk is a principle of progress for management science. We'll know we're getting somewhere when we don't have to take ourselves so seriously.

theoretical
management

To obey the prescription of Chapter Seven, management must look at itself as though it were "something other," for example, as a "science," or a way of knowing.

We can begin with two frustratingly elusive terms of science: *theory* and *fact*. The frustration comes about because in science we seem so sure at times what these ideas must mean, only to have them shattered by the next breakthrough in science history.

Now there is a perfectly reasonable sense, historically justifiable, in which *theoretical* is a property of a language man uses to describe and predict the world about him, that is, a property of the language of science. But there is also a reasonable sense, also historically justifiable, in which *theoretical* is a property of the way in which man makes decisions in his world. It is this second sense, the managerial sense of *theoretical*, that will concern us here. Hence we'll be exploring the concept of theoretical management.

The historical justification of the concept of theoretical behavior goes back many centuries, to the early Greeks. In more modern times it arises in the fascinating notion that knowledge is a way of doing or, as we have put it in this book, a certain kind of management of affairs. In other words, knowledge may be written in our actions as well as in our letters. The life of a successful manager may depict knowledge as readily as does an esoteric essay of some discipline.

To say that management is a kind of science is to imply that the validity of our ideas can be tested in the context of decision making. If the decision making is uniformly good, then the "principles" that produced the decisions are "valid," even though they may themselves be actions or attitudes.

Hence, to discuss a "theory of management" is to discuss a mode of managing, and not to develop a "model" of the management process. But how shall we distinguish between theoretical and non-theoretical management, and does the distinction make a difference in the practical managing, say, of firms or government agencies?

To find some guidelines, we should traverse briefly the old pathways of man's pursuit of the elusive concept of theory in science. Perhaps the best beginning is with Democritus of the fifth century B.C. His was an attempt to describe the behavior of all Nature in terms of a very few properties; the size, shape, and velocity of particles. Few would deny that Democritus sought a "theory" of Nature. What makes his work seem theoretical is (1) the parsimony of properties (Nature is "basically" made up of very few properties), and (2) the utter "rationality" of the laws (events must happen in one way only).

Both points are important in the subsequent history of ideas. Both Plato in his *Timaeus* and Euclid in his *Elements* try to reconstruct the whole or a part of Nature by means of a few basic properties, and both writers assume that Nature is inherently "rational" in its structure, that is, operates in one way.

If we are to characterize Euclid as a manager, we would say that he ran his enterprise with a strong central policy based on the assumption that the underlying structure of the world can be recognized, and once recognized, the policy can operate successfully thereafter.

This conviction that Nature is inherently rational characterized the early theorists of the Greek period. The irrational for them is inherent in man and his attitudes toward Nature; the goodness of man for the Stoics consists in man's learning the true rationality of his environment and adapting the right attitude toward it.

The same spirit pervades in the renaissance of science and philosophy in the seventeenth century. Leibniz tells us that there are various ways in which decision makers manage their affairs, but the most perfect manager is God. God requires no information from outside, and perceives all things analytically, that is, deduces all events precisely and perfectly. He is an ideal, self-contained inquiring system; for example, the time required to compute any finding, no matter how complicated, is exactly zero. The less ideal minds of Leibniz's world perceive less clearly, compute more slowly, make more errors, and have to use information as a crutch to compensate for their inadequacies. Reality is supremely rational: Minds of finite intelligence introduce noise, uncertainty, obscurity, irrationality.

It was the empiricists of the seventeenth and eighteenth centuries who argued so strongly against this type of theoretical manager. For John Locke, the mind starts with very little, and only after a long struggle does it come to learn about the rationality of the world. It starts by being meagerly theoretical. Nevertheless, Locke did maintain the other facet of Platonic theory: There are only a few basic qualities that the mind begins with. Everything is constructed from these few types of input to the system.

The most significant thing that Locke did was to place the rationality of the world in the inquirer himself. Or rather, to be historically accurate, it was Hume and especially Kant who showed that a mind that learns only from raw inputs must build in its own connections between these inputs. In Kant's philosophy, the inputs are so raw that the inquiring system cannot tell them apart unless it imposes a rationality upon them. "Telling apart" requires a concept of space and time, and the laws of space and time are the contribution of the inquirer, not something given to the inquirer.

In management terms, Kant's thesis is that information is as much a matter of managing as other practical decisions the manager makes. The most important managerial decision to be made about information is interpretation. Interpretation of information is a matter of inferring what the information means. If the manager is willing to assume a great deal about reality, he will interpret information in very rich terms, whereas if he is sceptical about how reality is going to behave, he will interpret information in very sparse terms. For example, a sales manager may asusme that his markets are all stable; he interprets last year's data to imply an accurate picture of this year's demand. Another manager may not want to assume anything at all about the stability of demand; he interprets last year's sales to be last year's sales and nothing else. It is to be emphasized that these two managers could not resolve their conflict by hiring an expert statistician according to today's concept of statistics. The statistician himself adopts either strong assumptions about reality or very weak assumptions; what makes him an expert is not contained in his willingness to assume or not to assume.

Now both these managers understand their problem to be one of using information that is in some sense given. The question is: Given by what? By a rational outside world? If all we have is what is given, then this "outside" world is unknown, unconscious, unreflective, and (as Berkeley put it) unnecessary.

David Hume tried to show that the so-called regularity of these inputs, and the conviction that they will reoccur in the same patterns as they had in the past, is a matter of habit of the mind. The manager simply becomes used to regularity.

The tactical problem of these managers is therefore one of deciding how much order to impose on what is given. Immanuel Kant tried to provide one guide for the manager in this connection. His thesis is that the manager must impose a minimal rationality because otherwise he won't be able to recognize any information at all. Specifically, he must assume that he can divide the world into the past and the future, and that objects can be structured in space. To do this, the information system requires a clock and geometrical measuring rods. The clocks and the rods presuppose a modicum of logic, arithmetic, geometry, kinematics, and mechanics. In other words, numbers, points, lines, planes, spaces, times, and masses exist because the information system operates that way, and we know of no other way for it to operate.

Although Kant showed to his own satisfaction that there must be a future if there is a past, he provided no help in showing what this future must be. It must be a future with a clock, a ruler, and a compass. But this is small consolation to a skittish manager who believes that Nature—including his competitors—may trick him, unless one could show (which Kant could not) that a world with a clock must be highly predictable.

Thus, there are two types of information managers, the bold and the cautious. Since neither manager is theoretical in the sense of Democritus, Plato, and Leibniz, let us call the bold one the generalizer, and the cautious one the particularizer.

The particularizer says that one cannot forecast. He likes to show how past attempts to forecast prices have been no better than random predictions, and then—very inconsistently to be sure—he asserts that therefore no one can forecast: *He* forecasts an infinity of failures to beat chance. The generalizer believes that the task is to interpret the data, and that interpretation includes the art of making a priori assumptions. So he tries, over and over, to predict what will happen, and he acts on his assumptions. Both particularizer and generalizer are fundamentally sceptical about the basic rationality of Nature: The flow of inputs may be—or may not be—a pattern. The flow is essentially nonrational, that is, does not originate from known rational causes.

Thus the bit of the history of thought we have just reviewed reveals three ways of managing information:

1. (Theorizer) A management based on the assumption that reality is rational (predictable); hence the task of the manager is to remove the randomness and obscurity of his own thinking, to become as much like reality as possible.

2. (Generalizer) A management based on the assumption that reality is nonrational, but that the task of the manager is to construct a strong structure within which the raw inputs from reality may be given the fullest possible weight.

3. (Particularizer) A management based on the assumption that reality is irrelevant, and that the task of the manager is to permit maximum flexibility of decision making so as to meet the requirements imposed by the data.

In language more familiar to the student of management, the particularizer is an opportunist, the generalizer a planner, the theoretician an idealist.

To delve more deeply into these categories, it may be of help to indulge in some formalism. The formal description assumes that the life of any decision maker may be considered as a string of decisions made at specific points of time. At these points of time, the decision maker has choices. Therefore, throughout his history he is creating his life by choosing one decision rather than another. At the beginning he confronts a fantastic array of alternative lives, and as he nears the end he finally decides just one life, which is his biography.

Assume that there is a value that can be assigned to any life-in-prospect of the decision maker. For purposes of discussion, also assume that this value can be fully described by a number on a scale. Thus each possible life L_1, L_2, L_3, etc., is a member of a class of lives, L, and associated with each life, L_i, is a value V_i. Each L_i is a string of decisions D_{jk}. The subscript j refers to the point in time, the subscript k to the particular physical decision that might occur at such a point. Thus j ranges over the decision-making episodes of the life, while k ranges over the alternative decisions that can be made at any episode.

Now suppose L_i is a life with a string of decisions D_{jk}. The notation $L_i - D_{jk}$ designates a class of lives in which, at time t_j, the decision D_{jk} does not occur, though every other decision in L_i remains the same. In other words, at time t_j, $L_i - D_{jk}$ contains a decision other than D_{jk}. (We note that the operator "$-$" is intended to be closed with respect to L; that is, given any L_i with D_{jk} at time t_k, there exists at least one L_m belonging to L which is like L_i in all respects except that it does not contain D_{jk} at t_k.) We assume that the value of L_i differs from the value of any member of $L_i - D_{jk}$, because otherwise a decision would not "make a difference" in the life of the individual.

Next we introduce the concept of a policy. A policy is a life, or a segment of a life, with an underlying theme. That is, an observer of the life can depict the pattern of the life by some rule. He sees, for example, that the life was trying to accomplish a goal, or avoid a certain kind of act. Evidently we are struggling to define something here that is quite obscure. To avoid the obscurity, without really solving the problem, we introduce a set of rules R. A rule is a device that at any time t_k selects a proper nonempty subset of the alternative decisions. If it selects one and only one decision at each t it is a rigid rule, whereas if it selects more than one (but not all) it is a constraining rule. Thus each rule selects a proper subclass of L. We say that a life is governed by a policy if it belongs to the subclass selected by some member of R.

As mentioned before, this way of defining policies does not really solve the basic problem, because one can always define a rigid rule for any life historically, simply by having the rule select the decisions that actually were made. The intent, of course, is that R contain only rules that the decision maker himself generated at the outset of a series of decisions.

To make this stipulation more precise, we introduce the concept of a *preparatory* decision. One decision prepares the way for another decision if it makes the latter possible. Thus the class of decisions that can be made at a point in time may depend on the decisions that were made earlier (one needs to decide to buy raw material if one wishes later on to decide to make a product). If a decision D_{11} at t_1 is necessary in order that a decision D_{21} be available at t_2, we say that D_{11} is a prepartory decision relative to D_{21}. A more general and more useful way to define preparation is to say that D_{11} prepares for D_{21} if all lives containing both have higher value than the corresponding lives containing D_{21} but not D_{11}.

A preparatory decision can be regarded as a planning action. Now in all discussions of planning, the cost of planning becomes important. Let us suppose that D_{11} is preparatory to D_{21} in the strong sense introduced above; that is, D_{21} can only occur if D_{11} precedes it. Compare now the set of lives containing D_{11} but not D_{21}, with the set containing neither D_{11} nor D_{21}. In each set there is an optimal life with its associated value. Let V_1 be the value of the best life of the set containing D_{11} but not D_{21}, and V_2 be the value of the best life containing neither. The difference $V_2 - V_1$ is the cost of preparing for D_{21} by adopting D_{11}. This fairly elaborate way to define preparatory decisions is chosen to be able to describe any kind of decision maker and his life, whether living or machine, individual or social. In lives with a heavy emphasis on preparatory decisions, the decision maker is a planner. He puts a lot of his potential resources into setting up for later decisions. Indeed, if we think of preparatory decisions in the same way in which we think of set-up procedures in production, then we can say that the set-up cost is a decision itself, and that the planner believes that planning is well worth the cost of the preparatory decision. Continuing the analogy with production, this means that the planner tends to make strong commitments, just as a high set-up cost in inventory theory implies large inventories.

To make the concept of a commitment clearer, we can return to the formalism introduced above. The lives of decision makers are pathways of decisions. Sometimes the pathways break into many choices at each episode, while at other times there are very few choices. In some cases the decision maker will start to follow one path, that is, to adopt one theme, but may find that this theme is unsatisfactory. If he has left himself flexible, he can change his theme without drastically changing the over-all value of his life, whereas if he has committed himself, he cannot feasibly reverse his theme. Thus a life is reversible if, once a decision has been made, it is possible later on to adopt other decisions that nullify the cost of the first decision.

To make this concept of reversibility clearer, suppose a decision maker has adopted decision D_{11} at time t_1. He now pursues his life until t_j, when he comes to regret his earlier choice. At this point, there may be a decision D_{j1} available to him that nullifies the effect of D_{11}. In other words, at t_j he can choose a life containing D_{j1} with a value equal to a life not containing D_{11}. He can pursue his life "as though" D_{11} had never occurred. A decision D_{11} is purely reversible at time t_j if there exist in L two lives with the following properties: (a) one contains D_{11} and the other does not, (b) both contain the same decisions between t_1 and t_j, (c) the one containing D_{11} does not contain D_{j1} at time t_j, while the other does, (d) the lives are the same after t_j, (e) the life containing D_{j1} is at least as valuable as the other.

A decision is irreversible if no decision can reverse it at a later period of time during the life of the decision maker. Evidently reversibility could become a matter of degree, depending on how much a later decision can erase the "cost" introduced by an earlier one.

I assume that the more a life tends toward preparatory decisions, the greater the irreversibility of its decisions. In other words, one who plans thoroughly commits himself to the decisions his plan dictates.

The planner, then, is one who adopts policies (lives with a theme) with preparatory and consequently irreversible decisions. The opportunist prepares minimally, and commits himself least; the theme of his life is much more difficult to discern except in vague terms like happiness or profit maximization.

The opportunist, therefore, lets the day-to-day data tell him how to respond. He is the operationally oriented manager in the sense that he tries to overcome the difficulties as they occur. One could only find a theme for his life if one could forecast the difficulties; but forecasting is a preparatory decision he tends to shun.

Nothing in the above discussion indicates which manager is "best," and man has always recognized the problem of prejudging either life by posing contradictory maxims: "Rome (Oh Great Irreversible Decision!) was not built in a day," and "He who hesitates (plans?) is lost."

The planning manager leads a life very much like the cognitive life of a so-called theoretical scientist. The opportunistic scientist plans minimally for the next experiment and lets the results of the experiment tell him what to do next. Today he finds contentment in the application of experimental designs and the analysis of variance and covariance. He thinks of himself as exploring a vast area, and being able to travel from one site to another with no loss of energy. Since he has no real a priori conviction about the outcome of an experiment, he is rarely disappointed intellectually. The generalizer, on the other hand, works for months building up an elaborate conceptual structure; only then does he permit himself to test his concepts. He can be terribly disappointed or marvelously overjoyed. But in either event, the next choice becomes an outcome of his preparatory structure building. Like it or not, his intellectual decisions tend to become less and less reversible the older he gets. A single datum, on the other hand, tends to become more and more important.

As for the generalizing manager, he believes in long-range planning, operations research, systems design, and all the other tools of management that emphasize the larger point of view. The opportunist believes in cases, daily or weekly accounts, and other "factual" reports. He believes in seeing his subordinates on the scene. He believes that on-the-spot tactics are more important than vague and general strategies.

If one were to try to characterize the shift in management that has occurred in the last two decades in America, it would be safe to say that it has become less opportunist and more planning.

What of management theory, then? The beginning of this chapter argued that there is a distinction between the true theorizer and the generalizer. Now, in the discussions of science this distinction is rarely made because the American scientific community has practically forgotten the rationalist philosophy that initiated its modern history. I said that the theorizer believes that reality is rational, and that rationality, randomness, and the like are the making of the inquiring mind. The generalizer, on the other hand, believes in order too, but he believes that order is what he imposes on chaos.

To the mind of Leibniz's God, there is no "given." "Data," for Leibniz, are the devices that poorer minds use to cope with reality; data are contingent, uncertain, obscure. Yet a modern scientist would argue that objectivity, the cornerstone of science, is to be found in data—what is given. The planning manager tries his best to prepare for what will come, but he ultimately believes that what will come will be given to him, as an "input." "Information" is the input he cannot plan. Or can he?

Suppose he asks himself this question: After all, since my plans do change the world, and hence also the information I eventually receive, what is it that my plans cannot change—what is really, fundamentally, irretrievably given? If he does ask himself this question, he is on the way to becoming a theorizer as well as a generalizer.

One response he may make is this: The past is irretrievably given. It is given that last year we sold 1,000 items of so-and-so. But is it? In the life of the manager, it is not what was sold that matters, but why it was sold. Can he create an answer to the *why*?

Suppose we are observing a man looking at a white swan. One question he could pose to himself is: Given this white swan, are all swans white? Another and more interesting question is this: To what degree is this a white swan? A manager may ask: Given these sales last year, what will the sales be next year? Another and far more interesting question is: To what degree is this a sale? As soon as we begin to regard Nature in depth rather than extension, we ask why rather than what. To learn that a swan has degrees of whiteness is to learn why the swan appears white to our eyes. To learn that a customer is sold in degrees of conviction is to learn why he appears to be someone we sold to last year. In both cases, the *given* becomes the start of a problem, not an answer. To ask why a swan appears white is the start of an inquiry in which the so-called induction to "all swans are white" is irrelevant. It is to understand that recording a swan as white is a delicate decision. To ask why a customer appears to be sold is also the start of an inquiry in which forecasts of next year's sales based on this year's sales are irrelevant. It is to understand that recording a sale is delicate decision. To record some transaction as a sale when the customer is truly dissatisfied, or truly erratic, or truly dead, is to make a foolish decision.

The theorizer is therefore the supreme questioner. He questions in depth as well as extension. Now one of the greatest insights of modern philosophy is E. A. Singer's dictum that to ask a question is to assume an answer. The question-asker assumes that answers *exist*. He also assumes that any reply he may give to an answer is no more than one response among many. *The* answer is an ideal, and yet it must exist. Reality is the ideal end of all question asking.

When a decision maker lives his life, he asks a question. The empiricist believes that when the life is over, then finally the answer to the question will be given. At this point, at life's end, the question-asker is, for the planner and opportunist, completely passive. To the theorizer, a life is also a question, but at its end there is only a response, one part of the whole that makes up the final answer. He believes that all these responses, in some rational but obscure way, go to make up the meaning of a life. The way is obscure, because we cannot accept the simple rationality of our philosophical predecessors, who defined the rational as the logically consistent. Whatever modern rationality is, it must be far richer in meaning than the logically consistent: It must include contradicion, opposition, conflict, evil, as well as consistency, sameness, cooperation, and good.

But how can all this talk about theory be translated into a type of management, that is, the choice of a life? The answer must be that to the theorizer, a life is a preparation for another life. That is, the observer can interpret the whole life as a preparatory decision. The *theory* of the active life of such a manager could be described as the collection of decisions that the manager believed his life prepared for.

This view of the theoretical manager is an old theme: It is the life that is led for the salvation of the soul, for an "after life." But the after life need not belong to the same soul or the same ego. It may be the after life of some organization, some discipline, some political party, some other person. We are all theoretical when it comes to our children, because we make decisions that will prepare for their lives. We may be far less theoretical when we vote for social change, or invest our money; then the only life that concerns us may be the life of the present, and we turn back to being opportunistic. One sees with a vengeance the meaning of the oft-quoted phrase "this is all right in theory, but not in practice." It means "this is all right as a preparation for another life, but all wrong for this life."

Finally, we should note that this labeling of lives by *opportunist, planner, theorizer,* is itself a choice, a choice of a biographer. One biographer may detect a policy, a plan, or even a theory in a life that another regards solely as opportunistic. And these choices of biography are not minor episodes, nor are they made solely by those who write and publish. For the most significant decisions of our lives are those in which we decide about the lives of others; our lives express our account of the biographies of those we love and hate.

large models
of systems

The past few chapters have explored the idea that rationality means looking at the same world from many different viewpoints. It's a difficult idea and tentative at best. For one thing, how do we know that one viewpoint is different from another? How do we know that many viewpoints, despite their differences, portray more than a small part of reality? The only feasible answer, of course, is to say that the differences and completeness are to be tested by the richness of human experience throughout its history. Historically, the viewpoint of a biologist differs from the viewpoint of a physicist or a psychologist. If at some time some smart young man really succeeds in "reducing" biology to an information code, then the viewpoint of the biologist may no longer be different from the viewpoint of the physicist. But one has to assess the likelihood of these reductions as best one can. In the case of a reductionist biology, one is apt to feel that all the life has been taken out of the model, so that the biological viewpoint is no longer portrayed. As for completeness, we try as best we can to learn about the different ways that people have looked at their world. An anthropologist would suggest a classification of viewpoints based on culture. A humanist would suggest a classification of viewpoints based on literature and the arts. An historian of science would want to classify different approaches to inquiry. A systems scientist makes classifications by types of system. And so on.

In the face of the inherent vagueness of the concept of rationality proposed in this book, the more precise mind will undoubtedly wish to return to older and more proven pathways to truth. Specifically, he may ask whether there is not one model that can be expanded and modified gradually and carefully, so the picture of the "whole system" may be approached. Indeed, the richness of mathematical modeling seems to make this suggestion quite attractive.

If we explore this idea of a larger and larger model of systems, we may be able to see in what sense completeness represents a challenge to reason. One model that seems to be a good candidate for completeness is called an *allocation* model; it views the world as a system of activities that use resources to "output" usable products.

The process of reasoning in this model is very simple. One searches for a central quantitative measure of system performance, which has the characteristic: the more of this quantity the better. For example, the more profit a firm makes the better. The more qualified students a university graduates, the better. The more food we produce, the better. It will turn out that the particular choice of the measure of system performance is not critical, so long as it is a measure of general concern.

We take this desirable measure of performance and relate it to the feasible activities of the system. The activities may be the operations of various manufacturing plants, of schools and universities, of farms, and so on. Each significant activity contributes to the desirable quantity in some recognizable way. The contribution, in fact, can often be expressed in a mathematical function that maps the amount of activity onto the amount of the desirable quantity. The more sales of a certain product, the higher the profit of a firm. The more courses we teach, the more graduates we have. The more fertilizer we use, the more food.

We call the mathematics that relates activities to the desirable quantity the *objective function*. The objective function is a basic ingredient of the allocation model's rationalization of systems, but it is not a sufficient ingredient. It is true that American culture loves large amounts of almost anything that Americans like: cigarettes, popcorn, candy, autos, pool halls, bars, restaurants, schools, zoos, and politicians. But in each case there are limits, largely arising from the fact that our cupidity is so diversified. Too many cigarettes produce a lessening of fresh air, which we want in more quantity. Too much candy lessens slimness, which we want more of. Too much of one product reduces the number of other products we can make. Hence any quantity we use as the measure of system performance must be constrained by considerations of other desirable quantities.

We handle the conflicting cupidities of human beings by what are called *constraint equations*. We now say that we want to maximize the objective function, subject to a set of constraint equations. Thus we can say that we wish to maximize the gross national product of an economy, subject to the constraints that everyone receives an education through high school, that every city has ten square feet of recreational space per inhabitant, and so on. We should note that the so-called intangible values can easily be written into this model, so long as we can state them in our equations: e.g., the need for safety precautions can be expressed as a constraint equation.

The problem is to maximize the measure of performance within the constraints. The solution of this mathematical problem is most prominently associated with the name of Lagrange. But in size we have gone far beyond anything that mathematicians of a century ago ever envisioned. According to one account, we can handle a particular mathematical system with a million variables and thirty thousand constraint equations (by means of what is called the *decomposition algorithm*). Applied mathematics of today can be characterized by the Texan syndrome: It may not be very elegant, but it is big.

We can also describe systems in many different ways: The functions can be linear or nonlinear, the variables may take on discrete or continuous values, they may be deterministic or probabilistic, and so on. The system may look like a network of fantastic size, described in a dynamic fashion. When all our mathematical ingenuity fails, we can use large computers to simulate the system, and very ingenious techniques to "search for" the maxima of our functions.

All this must sound very impressive indeed, especially when one reflects where we were a scant twenty years ago. At that time there were no techniques for the solution of even modestly large mathematical systems, except by old-fashioned and extremely laborious methods. Imagine trying to solve a set of linear equations with thirty unknowns by hand!

Grant that we can roughly measure the size of a mathematical system by the number of variables and equations, and that something like twenty variables and ten equations characterized 1945, and one million variables and thirty thousand equations characterizes 1965. If the growth is exponential, then perhaps by the time of Orwell's year 1984 we can handle systems up to 100 billion unknowns and 100 million constraint equations!

That would be quite a bit of rationalization. We should then, for example, be able to rationalize a large company like General Electric and its hundred or so divisions. Or we might even be able to rationalize a large part of the Federal government.

What can we say about this prospect? Should we look forward to a day when our government and industry will finally stop operating in a piecemeal, irrational way, and when all the major interdependencies will be considered in a precise and rational fashion? All we would need to do, you see, is write down what we want our Federal or local government to accomplish, and all the reasonable constraints we wish to impose on it in terms of money, time, and other resources. The model would be written in computer code, and the solution would tell each agency how it should behave. The model could conceivably be updated daily or weekly, and there we are.

Where? Has human initiative disappeared? Is there anything left in the decision process that is human at all?

Well, of course there is still a lot of humanity engaged in the large-model rationalizing we have just described. After all, humans have to write down their specifications—their objectives and constraints. All the models do is to rationalize what humans feel they want. But it is important to note that if people write down ridiculous constraints, the models can tell them how foolish they are. By means of a technique (often labeled as the *dual*) one can judge how costly a constraint really is, and hence whether it should be relaxed or tightened. Thus if we require ten square feet of recreation per city inhabitant, we may find that this is equivalent to a "cost" of one hundred dollars a year per person, and therefore see that the requirement is ridiculously costly. Hence we would systematically modify the constraints until they appear to be "reasonable."

Thus—in some age to come—we may perhaps merely say what we want and describe to a computer what we are able or willing to do, and our laws will be printed out for us. We won't understand why the results are what they are, because we won't be able to follow through the enormous computations—but we will be rationalized—won't we?

It is interesting to observe that the usual negative response to this question seems largely irrelevant. People want to say that we cannot quantify human values, nor can we put our trust in the computer. But we can and do quantify values all the time, in terms of dollars, or numbers of people, or houses, or deaths. In fact, *quantity* is simply one very ingenious and general way that man has found to describe his world, and there is really nothing basically wrong with this mode of description for those who like to use it. Besides, quantitative and qualitative descriptions are often intertranslatable. And as for a lack of faith in computer calculation, this seems to be the totally wrong place to be suspicious. Granted that computers can go wrong (or, more accurately, can be programmed incorrectly), they are no different in this respect from other pieces of machinery like autos, aircraft, and buildings in which we put our trust without much thought at all. Actually, more attention seems to be spent in the computer industry on safety and reliability than in most other large equipment industries.

No, the question of whether we shall put our faith in large models is not answered by either a distrust of quantity or high-speed computation. The question, indeed, is a philosophical one that belongs to the very difficult and generally neglected area of the philosophy of inquiry. It is not a new question at all. Plato in the *Timaeus* and his contemporary Democritus in writings that did not survive both seemed to have believed it possible to sweep the entire world into an ever-expanding model. Their belief was echoed down the ages—in Spinoza's *Ethics*, in nineteenth-century mechanism and evolutionism, and now today in a philosophy that is often used to sell system science and operations research. Nothing, it is said, can escape the eventual embrace of rational models.

The trouble with this philosophy is that it is wrong, dangerously wrong, pigheadedly wrong, philosophically inexcusable. It is not easy to say why it is wrong, because its basic idea is so attractive to narrow-minded but brilliant-thinking types. But if anyone will pause for a moment and reflect, he is bound to see the serious flaw.

The flaw is an unforgivable neglect of the problem of information. The philosophy I've just called wrong assumes that information is *here*, or if not here can be obtained. It's like the story of a very serious-minded young psychiatrist who addressed a group of patients in a mental hospital in a paternalistic fashion. "*Why*, my friends," he asked, "why are we all here?" "Because," a voice boomed from the back row, "we're not all there."

It is a common habit of mind to accept reality as something fixed, out there, that we can question in various ways by means of our senses, or our senses aided by instruments. Indeed, as mentioned earlier, the narrow-minded scientist referred to above likes to call this reality *Nature* (he seems to shy away from calling her Mother Nature, but he often treats her like a woman). He speaks of *states of Nature* or *moves of Nature*. He assumes that Nature is a creature he can address questions to and from whom he can receive direct answers. Thus he acts as though the facts about Nature can be "plugged into" his models, and therefore the models are realistic because they simply describe the states of Nature.

But this metaphysics is utterly naïve, and is the very reason the whole philosophy of the model builder is wrong. Consider, for example, a very elementary piece of "information" that is needed to build the allocation model: the cost of performing x units of an activity. How do I ask Mother Nature this question? One suggestion is to go to the records and add up the labor and material costs of past labor and material prices. Is this an answer to my question? Clearly not, because it may happen that the prices paid for labor and materials in the past were the wrong prices—the activity could easily have been mismanaged. My real question is: What is the cost when the activity is carried out properly? But how do I ask Nature this question? Which one of my senses do I use to obtain a direct answer? The only reply seems to be: You don't just use your senses; you must also reason about the activity.

Recall an example discussed earlier: the branch bank. It is a subsystem of the financial system. We can surely look forward some day to modeling the financial system of the U.S.A., and hence we shall sweep in the branch banks. How? We could describe them in terms of customer requirements, and service units of various kinds, and our model would then try to optimize the operations of the branch bank. But wait a bit. What is this subsystem trying to accomplish? Let's say that a large part of its objective is the storing and retrieval of financial information. If so, is this the kind of subsystem we need to do the job? It seems ridiculous to ask people to carry around financial information and transmit it in a haphazard fashion. Perhaps the whole subsystem should be redesigned. Perhaps we could easily eliminate checks and bank notes, which are surely very antiquated information devices.

Now note that a straightforward model builder of the financial system would never have "asked Nature" any question about the appropriateness of the subsystem—he would simply have "inputted" the data he found.

Of course, we could design such questions into the model-building process. We could insist that the model builder ask whether the activity has been well managed or whether the subsystem is appropriate. But how shall he get his answers? To determine whether an activity has been well managed, we need to see its relationship to other activities. To determine whether a subsystem is appropriate, we need to understand the whole system of which it is a part.

Now we can begin to see what is wrong with the claim that large models can sweep in all reality. The models don't mean anything unless they use the correct information. But we can't determine what information is correct unless we understand how the subsystems ought to be interrelated, or unless we understand the whole system. But this is what our realistic models are supposed to tell us. In other words, we need realistic information to start with in order to build our models, but we need the model to get the information.

In case there is some doubt about the seriousness of questions about subsystems, let me repeat some very reasonable questions about large systems that we may ask today:

(a) Do we really need private automobiles and freeways?

(b) Do we really need a very rapid transportation system?

(c) Do we really need separate schools and universities?

(d) Do we really need libraries?

We can't go to Nature with all these "do we really's" unless we understand what the whole world is like—because Nature doesn't give answers to these questions in a simple, unequivocal manner.

Suppose we state the same problem in another way. If we are trying to rationalize a system, we must consider that part of the system that is capable of implementing new plans. No matter how finely we construct our model, if the decision makers won't go along with the model's conclusions, the whole exercise is meaningless except as a purely game-like mathematical exercise. Now what questions can we address to Nature to get answers that will tell us how we can be confident of implementation? The truth of the matter is that none of us know or even have a fairly good idea of the questions. Do we need to know how to "sell" new ideas? Do we need to know how to "communicate" better? Do we need to sweep politics into our models? What is an optimal implementing system? Lots of people are trying to answer these questions today—but they differ in their answers, and none of them can justify what they say with *facts* gleaned from Nature's responses.

The point seems to be that we can't get facts about systems without making very strong assumptions about the systems.

Thus it looks as though we're involved in a vicious circle. We must get information to make our models realistic, but we must have general models to get our information.

Now there's a very direct way to answer all these philosophical questions. The answer is: Be practical! All this talk about the realism of the large model is fine in the abstract, but we've got to begin somewhere—so let's begin. The thing to do is start somewhere—with the feasible—and let experience modify our wrong guesses. Do something, so long as it works or looks as though it would work.

This seems to be the popular philosophy of the system-science enthusiasts in the political arena. For example, a recent study was conducted to develop a proposal for an information system for the State of California. Now the proposal certainly wasn't a full-fledged model, nor did it consider such questions as, "Do we really need a Department of Motor Vehicles," or "Do we really need educational records?" But it did say something that could be the basis of a beginning. The same practical philosophy seems to pervade the application of cost-effectiveness analysis, program budgeting, and similar techniques. They're all merely starting points—some things we can do *now*.

The trouble with this pragmatic philosophy is that it's *correct*, absolutely correct—mainly because it doesn't say anything at all. What it says is *do what is feasible*. Now if you don't know what *feasible* means, look it up and find that it means *capable of being done*. So this very wise and practical philosophy says *do what is capable of being done*. In some ways the opposite philosophy is preferable—*do what is incapable of being done*.

The problem, of course, is to find out what can be done that won't ruin us—take us down the irreversible pathways of self-destruction. If you try to pin the practical philosopher down to what he means by *feasible*, he becomes very elusive, if not downright abstract. Maybe he'll point out that in mathematical programming, a feasible solution is one that meets all the constraints. But he doesn't mean this when he talks about the feasible; for one thing, doing nothing at all is often a mathematically feasible solution, but none of these pragmatists would say that a do-nothing program is feasible.

No, what our practical, hard-nosed realist means by *feasible* is a plan that people will accept. He points out that many plans based on elaborate models are not feasible because no one will understand them, and people will resist them because they feel threatened.

The trouble is that once the practical philosopher moves away from his favorite tautology (*do only what you can do*) he gets into deep waters he himself doesn't understand. Politics is a subsystem of every large system. Resistance to suggestions is a part of politics. If

I say, "propose what people will not oppose," I'm telling you how to conduct your politics, and my advice may be very bad indeed. Sometimes politicians who try to avoid controversy are very bad politicians. The so-called practical philosophy of the feasible may really be based on a naïve or even stupid political premise.

Besides, I know enough about people to know how they love to deceive themselves. How many faculty meetings I've attended that have ended by a chairman's announcing "I think we can all agree . . . ," and on so many of these occasions what follows the announcement is the most unbelievable series of recommendations imaginable! We can all agree to do the stupidest things, especially since we all agree.

No, we should not base our planning on what is feasible at all, simply because this kind of down-to-earth practical philosophy is so much up in the air without any guarantee that it will fly.

What then? Should be abandon the attempt to rationalize human systems by large models? Certainly not. The "intuitives" are no better than the zealous rationalists. The intuitives like to say proudly and with textual inaccuracy, "our company just grew like Topsy," but "we've learned to fly by the seat of our pants," and "by a lot of work we've pulled ourselves up by our own bootstraps." The picture of a heavily booted and topless Topsy, driven by a turbine engine in her bottom, is probably typical of the conscious confusion that goes on in the mind of the managerial intuitive. There is less and less excuse for an ignorance about modern analytical technology on the part of today's top managers in industry and government. They are irresponsible if they pretend that the use of models and computers in their planning is "beyond them," or that they don't need to know about these newer developments because they've gotten so far without them. They are equally irresponsible if they expect to see positive results from planning models in one or two years at a minimum expenditure of time and effort. By this late date, intuitive managers should be realizing that an understanding of how their organizations really work is at least as difficult as an understanding of how a high-class rocket works. We live in an age of model building for decision making, and we can make this age the most significant of all time if we all work on the problem together.

After having thrown out the pure model builder, the pragmatist, and the intuitive, what is left? One great asset of the human race: Disagreement. Controversy.

Our fondness for being right and not being contradicted has led us into the acceptance of one of the three philosophies just discussed. The model-building rationalizer sees the world to be a world he can adequately and precisely describe mathematically. The practical philosopher sees the world to be the world of action —of compromise and doing. The intuitive sees the world to be one of his own making—made out of his genius. Well, each of these world makers tells us a story. He tells us what the world is really like and how we should cope with it. If our tribe were a smaller one, we could imagine that these three myth builders might in consecutive meetings each tell us the story of the future world in his own way. Each would have his heroes and his bad guys.

The heroes of the rationalist are brilliant men, scientists who can carve fine images of reality and, in the magic flash of colored lights, have their machines spell out what the next worlds will be like if we do certain things today. The villains of this story are the irrational piecemealers, selfish, shortsighted, dull of wit, endowed only with power.

The heroes of the practical philosophers are doers: They get people to adopt their ideas—to change a little bit here and there— in one spin-off or another—toward a better technological world. Their villain is the man who wrote on the wall of the Faculty Club at the University of California: "Whenever it is not necessary to change, it is necessary not to change." Their heroes are simple folk, who can talk sense to managers, who get things done, who accomplish change.

The heroes of the intuitives are the great leaders of government and industry, the fine gray-haired stern fathers who grace our boards of trustees, the judiciary, the professorial. They are wise and quick to respond when speed is essential, deliberate when deliberation is called for. Their villains are self-seeking interest groups, or dissidents of one kind or another who don't recognize their proper roles.

All these storytellers tell us fascinating tales, of horror or joy, of success or calamity. And whom shall we believe and have trust in? Who has the real insight? Which myth maker has his ear tuned to God?

Why, none of them and yet all of them. We are the listeners, and if we listen well we shall hear the differences as well as the sameness. It is not necessary for us folk of the tribe to believe wholeheartedly in what model builders say, any more than we need believe in practical men or wise men. But we should listen most carefully to the story that each has to tell.

And this brings us back to the theme of the large model. A large planning model is a story—it is one idea of what reality is like and what it could be like. It is a marvelously told story in its way —not dramatic perhaps, but as a mosaic of details it is unsurpassed. One can wander endlessly in the ramifications of the fabric of the tale, touching on this or that episode and the way it will affect our lives.

The main trouble with this type of storytelling is that the storytellers believe they must be consistent. Now no storyteller who is worth anything at all as a concocter of tales should ever try to be consistent. Certainly the man of action regards petty consistency as anathema, and the wise father-figures only use it as a political device when it suits their aims. There is no reason why all model builders have to tell the same story about the same system. This makes them very dull people.

I've a specific suggestion. Say a nation wants to know whether to prolong a war in which it is engaged. Some men of action tell us it's the only feasible course because how can we pull out? Other men of action tell us it's the wrong course because we must pull out. Some wise men, stroking their beardless faces, say we must stem the tide. Other wise men say we must face the music. What do model builders say? Nothing. They are too shy. They are afraid that their "information" or forecasts may be inadequate. Nonsense. Let us build two model-building storytellers. One will tell us what the world is really like, and his model world will interpret all the data to show that our current policy in Vietnam is correct. The other will tell us what the world is really like, and his model world will interpret all the data to show that our current policy is incorrect. The two worlds these storytellers will build are different, of course. It is up to us, the listeners, to see which one—if either—we are willing to accept.

Let's try this model-building controversy in all kinds of contexts —educational planning, poverty wars, health, urban development, and so on. After all, debate has long been the common practice of practical men and intuitive men—why not of rationalizers as well? Actually, rationalizers do debate among each other fiercely, as any one knows who's worked in a lively team of operations researchers. One member of the team will push for one viewpoint, and find himself strongly opposed by his colleagues. The trouble is, this debate is hidden when "briefings" are made to managers. Model builders think they should make one united, consistent proposal based on one model. The decision maker, therefore, loses out on the really crucial part of their study, the conflict of ideas that went into the model building.

But what of truth? What is the correct answer to the pressing problems of human systems? Well, there was one American philosopher, John Dewey, who showed that the quest for certainty is bound to fail, because certainty is an unattainable goal. There was another American philosopher, Edgar Singer, who put the matter more deeply and accurately: When we reach a conclusion after having exposed our ideas to the most severe test we can imagine, then we have done the best that inquiry can possibly accomplish.

The only trouble with Singer's wise saying is all the trouble in the world: How do we know we have exposed our ideas to the severest test? If we have bound ourselves by our thinking into one corner of reality, then we shall never expose ourselves to the really severe test. Instead, we shall wander aimlessly about in our own narrow muddle, thinking we are progressing, but getting nowhere at all. The possibility that we have become prisoners of our own concepts is a topic that demands a separate study in the next part.

part **III** the ethics
of whole
systems

realism and idealism

The last chapter ended with a challenge to reason: To establish by rational means the scope of alternative plans or pathways of progress. What assures us that in our attempts to improve social systems we have considered all that it is possible to consider?

There is another challenge, closely related to this one. All along we have talked about "whole systems" or "*the* whole system." Is there but one "whole" system, or many? Is the universe of reality made up of sectors with recognizable boundaries, so that each sector exists more or less independently of the rest? Or are the sectors so interrelated that only one "whole system" exists?

In this chapter let us look at these two challenges in terms of a theory of reality, or, alternatively, a theory of the realistic. In the next chapter we shall examine the same challenges in terms of the theory of the aesthetic, and in the last take up the challenges in terms of the theory of the good. The trilogy is a philosophical bias: The philosopher likes to divide the world of philosophical discussion into the real, the beautiful, and the good, although this division, too, is subject to a challenge.

The cast of characters of this chapter is made up of two extremists. The first is called a *realist*, and believes that reality is what exists in the world of the senses, the hard-fact world. He also believes that reality does not exist in "wholes." He is fond of saying that "there is no such thing as a group mind, or an organization, and certainly no such thing as a 'whole system'." He doesn't object to putting pieces of reality together into what he calls *constructs* but he cautions that these constructs are "secondary" or "conventions" or "inferences," and have no reality other than as words. Such a realist sees the first challenge to be a challenge to observation: How can we be sure we have observed all that is relevant? For him, there are many systems—as many as one wishes to construct. Consequently he is a *pluralist*, and his answer to the second challenge is: "It all depends on what you want to do." The second character is an *idealist*, and he has really been the central character of this book. For him the question "What is real?" means "What is realizable?" Since the realizable is an idea, he believes that ideas are primary; what we observe is the result of what we think about. Hence he interprets the first challenge to be a challenge to thought: How can we be sure that we have thought about everything that is relevant? Now this idealist may be a pluralist, because he may think about the realizable in different segments of his thought process. But I'm going to make him a *monist*, someone who is convinced that there is just one "whole" system, and that we can't divide up the problems of improving systems into sectors without running the severe risk of degrading rather than upgrading the whole system.

The idealist-monist has been the topic of discussion in the earlier chapters. Now we want to engage him in an on going debate with his old enemy, the realist-pluralist. But first, note that this is not just a debate between philosophers. Managers, the people who make decisions, also recognize a distinction between the "practical" decision maker and the "visionary" decision maker. In Chapter Twelve, I described this distinction in terms of short- versus long-range planning. The practical short-range planner believes that the only objectives that are realistic are those that we can see out to the "horizon." The visionary long-range planner believes that the only objectives that mean anything to us are those that determine our whole lives, that is, the objectives that lie beyond every horizon of human aspiration. The manager's debate is about what is *realistic*, the philosopher's is about what is *real*, but it's the same debate, nonetheless. In fact, philosophy will benefit considerably by putting its old-fashioned problem into the context of new-fashioned decision making.

Now, if we try to put the distinctions of either the philosopher or the man of affairs in the context of our thinking about large systems, both extremists tend to look ridiculous. The old-fashioned realist, when confronted with the meaning of the reality of systems, begins to look absurd just as the old-fashioned idealist does as he tries to explain the meaning of the "ideals" of systems. The same situation applies to the decision maker. The more he attempts to be feasible and realistic the more impractical he actually turns out to be. But the more the long-range planner talks about the ultimate goals of large-scale systems, the more vague he becomes.

Suppose we were to set about trying to describe a system—for example, a school system in an urban community. The hard-headed realist type, as well as his managerial counterpart, the practical man, would set about *observing* all that happens in the activities of the school during the day. He would try to understand what kinds of people and information flow into the school, how both students and information are processed, and what flow out as "finished products." From this set of "data" he would generate an "objective" description of how the school operates. When he is done and has tabulated his information in various ways, he would draw appropriate charts and even display a picture or two. He might then declare, in the mood of traditional empiricism, that his description is a real one in the sense that what it says accurately and validly describes the reality of the school system. A practical man of affairs might also want to argue that this description is realistic, in the sense that it provides the manager with a "sound" basis of knowing "exactly" what is going on in the system.

But now a thought occurs to us: What is the system after all that we are concerned with here? Evidently it is the system designed to "educate" a certain number of citizens. We might at this point begin to speculate that the *actual* form that the school system has taken in our society is accidental. The *facts* that people enter the school and that information is processed in various ways may have occurred as a result of various decisions made in the past that now are totally inadequate.

Consider, for example, that really antiquated technique called *rote learning*. Its objective is to store items in the memory of students: multiplication tables, spelling, historical facts, etc. The student is tested periodically to determine whether the items are in his memory, and whether he can retrieve them accurately. Rote learning is a fact about most modern school systems. But why do we have rote learning? Because later on in life the citizen will be required to retrieve these items from his memory. But note that the whole language I have used to describe the function of rote learning sounds very much like programming a computer; and since computers are and will be very excellent memory devices, this suggests that the need for certain types of rote learning will diminish. Perhaps we won't need to multiply or spell correctly, because a computer system can intervene between our actions and the output, and correct any errors we may make. Thus we might vastly reduce the dreary hours of a schoolboy's experience. Wouldn't we have to say that the empiricist and hard-headed man of affairs who had spent their time carefully observing and documenting the activities of the school system *as it is* are both incorrect in their observations and *unrealistic* in their approach to the problem? In fact, all the observations so carefully collected might turn out to be completely irrelevant. It would be as though someone were asked to describe a beautiful bird and described an ugly spider instead. The fact that something is there and is called *rote learning* is not the basis on which one can describe the facts about the school system if there is some other potential reality that far better serves the purposes of the system. The direct observer, in other words, is both factually incorrect and totally impractical. He is unrealistically realistic.

But what does the idealist or long-range planner say in this situation? Apparently what he says is that we must look at all alternative designs that a system could take on to satisfy its purposes and that the "real" system is the design that best serves the purposes. But this suggestion also seems to be totally unrealistic. How can we possibly look at all possible designs? How can we even understand what all possible designs mean unless we have taken some observations beforehand? We certainly can't think about alternative designs of large systems in the abstract. We can't let our ideas take care of all the problems of reality. But since the idealist wants to change the world to make it better, and his ideas are impotent, his idealism is far from being ideal.

Thus if we take the traditional notions of what a realist is and what an idealist is, both of them seem to be absurdly inadequate. If the realist believes that reality is what he directly apprehends and that this apprehension defines what a system is really like, then he turns out to be utterly unrealistic because he ignores the possibility of radically different designs. If he claims that what he cannot comprehend and observe is irrelevant until something causes it to become relevant, then he becomes a passive observer, a captive of his own observations. But if the idealist claims that the true constraints on systems design are those that ideas determine, then his ideas are in danger of becoming pure imagination.

At this point it seems necessary to become a bit more precise in order to make sure that we undersand what we are talking about. To this end, suppose we examine a more carefully defined problem, one in which the issue between long-range and short-range planning can be clearly stated. It is also one of the most mundane of all human problems: the production of goods for consumption. We should expect to find expressed in this activity the very essence of hard, worldly realism; we should expect that those who have assumed the responsibilities of producing goods have learned from their vast practical experience how to be realistic. The ineffable qualities of the idealist seem totally lacking here.

The practical problems that the manufacturer must try to solve are what items to make and how many to make. These two problems break down into a number of very important subproblems, concerned with quality, work methods, distribution, advertising, and the like. But for our purpose it will be sufficient to treat the producer's problem in a fairly simple and direct way.

Our realist or practical man of affairs will ask the question: What facilities does the producer *actually* control? He will argue that we need to know this to obtain a realistic notion of what the producer can produce if he wishes. His next question is: What does he hope to accomplish by producing? We will need to know this to obtain a realistic notion of what constitutes satisfactory output from the manufacturing plant. We note that both questions are "realistically" concerned with the world that immediately surrounds the producer.

To a realist, past history supplies two rather obvious answers to these questions. It tells us the kinds of products that the producer has been able to make in the past, and the kinds of results that he has deemed satisfactory. To describe precisely how the producer's realities shape his realistic plans, we can more precisely formulate the model of activity analysis described in very general terms in Chapter Thirteen. The manufacturing procedures that produce and distribute a specific product are what we there called an *activity*. The amount of this activity can be measured by the number of items of the product that is manufactured in a given period of time.

If we have been successful in classifying the products that the manufacturer can make, and in determining the technology of his plant, then we can designate the amount of any activity by x_i, denoting the ith product of our classification.

From the point of view of the model, the producer can now be described as someone who chooses a certain number for each activity. If there are n products, a given choice can be designated by the choice of a vector $(x_1, x_2, \ldots, x_i, \ldots, x_n)$, each x_i representing the amount of the corresponding activity. Of course at this point it begins to look as though idealism had slyly infiltrated into the realist's thinking. What does the producer *really* choose, a vector, or a line of real products? That is, does the producer choose an idea or real things? The idealist will say that the producer really chooses an idea, whereas the realist will say the producer really chooses the *actual* products. The realist will try to say that the model is a picture of reality and is not reality itself. The idealist will turn around and ask the realist, "In this situation what is reality?" If the realist then points to products and says that these are the real things in the world, the idealist will respond that these are not what the producer is deciding about. He is deciding about a number and not about the items that are observed.

Suppose, however, for the moment we stop this quarrel, simply noting that the realist reserves the right to discard the model out-right if he so chooses; he may banish model building from reality by a flick of his mind.

If we proceed along with the model and assume that the realist is patient, we can represent within the model how much return the producer can expect to obtain from making an amount x_i of the ith product. In the simplest case, this "returned value" of the ith product is proportional to the amount he produces and can thus be designated by x_i times a profit coefficient π_i. The producer's realistic interest is in maximizing the total returned value, that is, maximizing $\sum_{}^{n} \pi_i x_i$, the sums of the profits of each product.

The formal description we have introduced is an example of a model of activity analysis, and the simple relation between input and profit is an example of what is called *linear programming*. One further reality needs to be added to complete this model of the producer's world. His facility is limited in various ways. For example, each item takes a certain amount of time to produce. If it takes t_i hours to produce the ith product, and x_i are produced in a given period, then obviously the producer has committed $t_i x_i$ hours of his facility's time to make the ith product. If all together he has only T hours of time which he controls, then the $t_i x_i$ hours summed over all the products cannot exceed T, that is, in mathematical terms, $\sum_{}^{n} t_i x_i \leq T$.

Time may not be the only realistic constraint on the producer. For example, he has to worry about the total amount of capital available to pay wages, to buy equipment, to transport the products, etc. In the very succinct terms of mathematical programming, the producer's *real* problem is to choose a vector $(x_1, x_2, \ldots, x_n)$ that will maximize his profits, that is, maximize $\sum_{}^{n} \pi_i x_i$, subject to various constraints on the x_i's.

Now our realist is surely one who shies away from vague or general assumptions; indeed, in the case of a model like this one, he will only tolerate a very minimal number of straightforward assumptions. But what assumptions have been made in the technical picture of the producer that we have just outlined? To a mind like the realist's, which relies on logic and hard fact, the following assumptions might be permitted:

(a) *Assumptions based on logic*, for example,
    (i) the producer cannot realistically make both x_i *and* $x_i + 1$ items of the same product in any period; or
    (ii) some representation of the vector $(x_1, x_2, \ldots, x_n)$ must be realized in any period (including the vector with all zeroes); or
    (iii) x_i cannot be negative (that is, it is impossible to manufacture a negative number of products).

(b) *Assumptions based on the hard realities of the producer's world* (that is, on the technology available to him),
    (i) the return from x_i is $\pi_i x_i$ (that is, the profit the producer can make is proportional to the number of items of each product that he makes);

    (ii) $\sum\limits_{}^{n} t_i x_i \leq T$ (that is, the manufacturing time cannot exceed the maximum time available to the producer) and so on.

(c) *Assumptions based on the realities of the producer's aspirations*,
    (i) the producer always prefers that the sum of the $\pi_i x_i$'s be as large as possible (that is, the producer always prefers a larger profit to a smaller one).

(d) *Assumptions about what is realizable*,
    (i) any state of the producer's world containing the vector $(x_1, x_2, \ldots, x_n)$ is possible in the period provided the realistic constraints are satisfied;
    (ii) the producer can change any vector (within the constraints) to any other vector at a later period of time.

These assumptions seem to form a fairly precise basis of describing the producer's real world in terms that ought to satisfy both the realist and the practical man of affairs. The realist would say that the model is "realistic" if it accurately represents reality, and it accurately represents reality if *in fact* all the statements of the model are true: For example, if in fact profit increases in proportion to the amount of each activity.

But now the idealist or long-range planner will ask his continuously annoying question: Are the assumptions of the model realistic just because they are in fact true? The assumptions are something like the underlying assumptions in the case of the school system. They state what is in fact there, but what is in fact there may be largely irrelevant.

Thus the idealist cannot agree with the realist that the model is a realistic description of what the producer can do or what he can expect to gain just because it tells us the boundaries defined by the *factual* constraints. The idealist will claim that it is not unrealistic for the producer to try to make choices outside these factual boundaries. The idealist warns the producer to be wary of the realist's claim that his description provides realistic boundaries of the producer's choices. For example, the model claims that "as a matter of fact" the producer's choice cannot result in his exceeding time constraint T. Is this a realistic claim? Of course not. Why? Because we have an *idea* that the producer could exceed this constraint by buying or renting a new plant or by hiring new personnel, for example, by selling some stock he holds in another company. Although he is in fact constrained by his present technology and capital, he need not be. The fact of the constraint does not tell him what is realistic. Fact and reality are in this case based on an idea, or even an inspiration, says the idealist.

From a decision-making point of view the real constraint is not a "matter of fact," but a matter of value, that is, a matter of preference based on the decision maker's ideas about his world. If he does not "as a matter of preference" wish to borrow additional money, then this matter of preference establishes the reality of the existing constraint on the time available to him for production. In other words, the model does not in fact describe the world of the producer until it makes explicit the value status of constraints, but values are ideas in the head of the decision maker.

This is a very curious state of affairs. At first sight the constraints seem to be the most realistic aspects of the whole picture, for they seem to describe the hard-and-fixed reality that confines the producer. He cannot say, "I'd like to make millions of these items, because they will all make me a large profit." For him to say this would be to say something utterly unrealistic. What is realistic, then?

Why, at first glance, it is realistic to consider the plant, the workers, the engineers, the available cash. These realities imply constraints on the producer's actions. These constraints are realities just as much as a road block is a real constraint on the driver of a car. Now we find that this first glance is all wrong. The existing plant and its personnel do not define the real constraints on the producer, because he lives in a much larger world, and this larger world presents him with opportunities that can realistically modify the constraints. It is as though each purported constraint were a door to a larger reality; the door is a real barrier only if the producer chooses to keep it closed.

It begins to look as though the idealist is right. The real world of the producer is not what immediately surrounds him—his plant, personnel, money, products, etc. Instead his real world includes all the rest of the world that is relevant to his aspirations. If the producer is "narrow minded," his real world will be narrow, and he will do less imaginative and less risky kinds of things, like keeping his borrowing to a minimum and his research expenditures low. But he may suffer by adopting such a policy. Surely he is not a realist then.

We see now how the characters in the story become blurred and indistinguishable, because the realist has been pushed into a position very similar to that of the idealist: He must consider that nebulous, abstract idea called *whole system*; he must do this if he is to be realistic about his plans. He cannot avoid making strong assumptions because he must make certain assumptions about the whole-system preferences of the producer.

Thus it seems as though we can't keep the two characters of our story apart: The realist and idealist merge.

On the other hand, these two characters do seem to exist in the real-life story of human foibles. It is easy to recognize the "hard-headed" politician or businessman who shies away from abstract, nebulous ideas, who deals in tangibles, who wants the facts and not the theories, who above all exists in the world of the feasible. Whenever ideas drive him to consider superworlds and vague consequences, he abandons the idea for the world he can deal with. He is not a great, over all planner, but a man who charges in where real opportunity exists and deals with the factors that really matter.

Perhaps we can search for the distinction between the realist and the idealist by returning to the notion of a system. As I have said, in a system the parts have reality only by virtue of their relationship to other parts. The wheel of a car is *really* a wheel only because there is an axle and the axle is real only because there is a frame. These are very familiar connections between the parts of systems. We have been discussing a much more subtle systematic connection. We said that the time constraint on the number of items that could be produced was a real constraint only because the producer chose to construct his whole world in such a manner. In other words, this constraint follows from the value system of the producer. The reality of the time constraint is a consequence of the way in which the producer chooses to design the manufacturing part of his system with respect to his whole system.

It is true, as I have said, that the word *system* has many different meanings in discourse, but all along we are concerned with the design of systems to accomplish a set of purposes. From this point of view, the parts of the system bear special relationship to the whole; namely, in principle it should be possible to evaluate a part in terms of its *system effectiveness*, that is, in terms of its contribution to the attainment of the system objectives. More precisely, associated with each part we should in principle be able to determine an effectiveness measure; given a fixed state of the rest of the system, the more effective a part becomes (within specified limits) the better will be the whole system. The question of system design is directly concerned with this effectiveness measure. The question is whether this measure can be developed without having to make any assumptions about the whole system and its characteristics. In other words, is it possible to specify a *part objective* and a *part environment* which will be sufficient to determine a measure of effectiveness of the part?

Now we can suggest a solution to the distinction between the realist and the idealist. Perhaps we can say that a realist is one who believes in concentrating his attention on the parts, all other things being equal; he believes it is realistic for us simply to consider the part and not bother our heads about the obscure whole.

Consequently, when the realist looks at a system, he tries to examine where the troubles really are, and to do this he examines the behavior of each part. A Governor of the State of California once issued a mandate that all parts of the system reduce expenditures by 10 percent. This is an application of the realist philosophy because it is based on the notion that if one looks into each part, it will be possible to remove sufficient waste of time and money to make the required reduction in expenditure. One can do this part by part, says the realist, without having to concern oneself about the effect on the whole system.

In other words, to the realist a part can be realistically considered because the parts can be made *separable*. From the point of view of system design, separable parts can be considered *on their own grounds*, each being affected without the need to think explicitly of the whole system. Thus if the realist thinks of himself as an individual, he may decide to be an excellent entrepreneur, golfer, husband, and lover, and in each part of his life set specific goals appropriate for that part. Or the President of the U.S.A. may think that he can design an educational plan, an antipoverty plan, a defense plan, and a health plan, each as a separable program of his administration. The realist thinks he can perfect each part of his life or his nation without a strong reference to the other parts. But since no one is pure in any of the categories of human life, one should say that the realist is an individual who *tends* to try to look at the parts of the system as though they were separable.

Does this distinction really help? It seems to characterize the practical man of affairs, if not the classical realist. The practical man of affairs seems to believe that each problem can be handled on its own terms.

But the trouble is that the idealist has no difficulty whatsoever in making this description of the realist look silly. Suppose the realist argues that it's absolutely essential to reduce costs in each part by 10 percent. Probably this can be done. The idealist will point out that, if in principle it has been possible to reduce costs 10 percent in the past, then why haven't we? If the realist answers that people are careless, and that if they tighten their belts they can really accomplish the cost reduction, the idealist goes to work and shows how the parts are in fact not separable at all. For example, supposing one part of the government decides to cut costs by simply eliminating a function, such as the collection of health records, which it does not regard to be an essential part of its activities. Thus the school system might stop collecting health records of students on the expectation that these things could more adequately be done by the Health Department. But of course the Health Department is actually engaged in trying to accomplish a 10 percent reduction itself and cannot take on the additional load placed on it by the action of the Education Department.

The point, says the idealist and long-range planner, is not the reduction of costs per se but the way in which the reduction of costs spells out more effective or less effective plans of the society. One cannot perfect the operations of one component of the system without looking at the way in which this effectiveness is accomplished and the way in which it reacts with other parts of the system. Thus many realists become very puzzled and annoyed by what they consider the irrationalities of their social world, crime, slums, discrimination, cheating in social welfare; they wish to clear up the mess wherever they find it. But in their attempts to "improve things" they create disturbances in other parts of the system, disturbances that come back on them and forestall their improvements. We are all aware of the instances where, under the claim of instituting new freedoms, government agencies indulge in spying, wire tapping, suppressing freedom of speech and political action. Slums become cleared away only to be replaced by ugly parking lots, and the slum dwellers reappear in some other ghetto of the city. The idealist and long-range planner argue that the whole system has to be understood as a complex of competing parts, each wanting something that constrains the others. Consequently the parts of the system cannot be looked at as separable from one another.

Hence the notion that a realist is someone who believes in the separability of the parts of the system makes him look ridiculous.

So far we have been concentrating our attention on the realist. What about the idealist and long-range planner? They also come out to look quite ridiculous in the context of systems thinking.

If we take the idealist seriously, no one can act unless he knows the whole of reality, which he never will. The practical decision maker knows that he must act. The idealist and long-range planner ramble on endlessly about all kinds of ramifications and postpone the moment of action indefinitely. Indeed, in some cases it appears as though the planner is not interested in action at all. He is perfectly satisfied if he comes up with what he regards as a suitable plan. He becomes quite indifferent to the problem of how his plan can be implemented. Quite inconsistently, he assumes this to be somebody else's job: Suddenly he assumes his planning part is separate from the implementation part. Thus the idealist will talk about unilateral disarmament, or a scheme by which the nations of the world agree to be bonded and could be penalized for aggressive acts. Once he has suggested either of these plans he thinks his job is done; he is not concerned at all about how the plans could possibly get into action given the international political situation. The paradox of the idealist is that he himself believes in a vicious separability of thinking and action.

Perhaps here then is a basis on which we can find a distinction between our two characters. Suppose we say the practical aspect of the realist lies in his belief in action even when action entails risks. The realist in other words is sensitive to the problems of timing. The idealist on the other hand believes in the reality of the plan; the action is secondary.

In this distinction it's the realist who seems to come out on top, because he believes, along with common sense, in the reality of the act and the actor, the decision and the decision maker. Wonderful! The idealist of course, believing instead in the reality of the plan and especially the ideal plan, looks impractical and absurd.

But who is this actor, this hero of the realist philosophy? For example, in the model of the producer's world it was assumed that the producer was the actor who acted as a unit with a well-defined preference and with well-defined alternative choices. From the realist's point of view the actor and the action were embedded in this concept of the completely responsible and authoritative decision maker. This picture is sheer nonsense. The producer is not a unit, no matter how forceful a personality he may be. He is at least a coalition of many people—stockholders, government, consumers, labor, public. He is also a self, that is, a very complicated system of conflicting psychological beings, of ego and id, of persona and archetype.

But the realist may respond that it is convenient to consider the entrepreneur as a unit in much the same way that the astronomer considers the whole earth as a unit in calculating its orbit. In the astronomer's case, however, such a simplifying assumption may not "significantly" distort his results. The earth is admittedly not really a mass concentrated at one point, but it may not really matter if we think of it in this way to predict planetary motion. The unreality of the simplifying assumption is really unimportant. But we have no grounds for saying that the simplifying assumption about the producer is really unimportant. For example, if we are not careful, we are apt to perceive a great deal of irrationality in human beings when we look at them as analyzable units; they perform contradictory acts, or "refuse to pursue their own best interests," simply because in reality they are not units at all but complexes. A producer will refuse to make a product that will sell very well simply because he doesn't believe in it, or his father didn't, or the stockholders won't. The irrationality is in the mind of the observer, not the decision maker, because the observer insists on adopting an unrealistic simplifying assumption that the decision maker is a unit.

The paradox of the realist continues. He thinks that the actor and action are the basis of reality, but the actor and his action turn out to be two ideas in the head of the realist—and not very good ideas at that.

As the idealist sees it, the question is whether there are "ultimate parts" of systems, that is, parts that are not themselves decomposable into subparts. More specifically, the question is whether one can conceive of a part as a "black box" and not have to make assumptions about the interior of the box in judging the reality of the actions of the box. If the realist believes in action and actors, then he could be said to believe in the existence of black boxes in systems design. From the idealist's point of view the realist now turns out to be a silly kind of idealist, because he believes in an idea that has no justification in reality. The possibility of finding these ultimate units, the ultimate actor and action, is an impractical hope.

I have been searching without success for a distinction between realist and idealist within the context of systems design. Now something that we have mentioned earlier may help. Perhaps the difference between the two types lies in their concept of timing. Perhaps the realist is less bothered about the unexamined aspects of the problem than is the idealist. The idealist wants to spend more time trying to understand every aspect of the problem, whereas the realist wants to spend more time trying out solutions in action.

But unfortunately this distinction doesn't help either. Time, after all, is essentially an idea. If what is being discussed is the proper way to time the implementation of a plan, then from the idealist's point of view one must obviously think about *timing*. If the realist says that one should act without thinking, then the realist is simply unintelligent. If all the realist is saying is that timing is an important aspect of any plan, the idealist would agree with him completely. The meaning of timing is in fact well embedded in any rational plan. Furthermore, says the idealist, the person who wishes to escape assumption making shouldn't talk about timing because timing involves the strongest kinds of assumptions.

And there it is. Try as hard as you will, the distinctions simply disappear in the context of thinking about systems. The old-fashioned realist believes in some kind of reality out there. For him the model is a "representation" of reality. But then what does he mean by a representation of reality? What is being represented? If he says what is being represented is a sense experience, then what is sense experience? If sense experience is in the form of a language, for example, "it is yellow," "this is soft," then the language must have a grammar and a grammar is one form of a model. If a sense experience is a kind of mysterious happening that goes nameless, then what meaning does realism have after all? Is realism going to say that the meaning of reality depends ultimately on the mysterious and elusive?

Try as I will, I can't keep realism from looking absurd. The realist wants to thump hard, look hard, and "what happens" to him is supposed to be reality! He's not even childish, because even a child knows better than to trust his senses alone; the imaginary also complements the sensory in his reality.

Idealism is an absurdly easy philosophy because its opponent is so ridiculous.

Yet the strange situation still continues. Realism in our culture is the more popular philosophy. People admire the straightforward man of action, just as in science they admire the individual who does not drift off too vaguely into ill-defined theories.

The realist hero in the case of science is the so-called disinterested observer. This hero is supposed to inject as little of himself as possible into his reconstruction of reality. Admittedly, he is a man of passions, a man of the political scene, a cog of many wheels. But according to the realist all science needs of him is his ability to observe and reason dispassionately. The pictures he draws of reality thereby are supposed to become accurate, whatever may be his emotional life, or whatever may be the politics, poverty, and punishment of his age. According to the realist this dispassionate hero may even devoutly wish that Nature were otherwise, especially in the way She designs human nature, but his strict adherence to the standards of scientific conduct successfully wards off such inputs to the system.

But the idealist has no difficulty whatsoever in systematically destroying this realist hero, who thrives on the concept of this separable and disinterested observation.

As any student of the history of science knows, since the invention of the disinterested observer in the sixteenth and seventeenth centuries, much has been done to modify his character in order to maintain some feasible grounds for believing in his existence. The first inroads were small, though subtle. They came about because the disinterested observer could not conscientiously ignore his own contribution to the observation; it became necessary to study the psychology of observation.

The realist now sought to save his hero by introducing *direct observation*; by direct observation he meant that no instrument was involved. The so-called naked eye, he says, does not introduce instrumental biases. This is certainly a naïve position, considering what we know about optics, as well as response delays to stimuli. The re-

corded observation, say, of the position of a point in the visual field
is clearly the result of the very fine instrumentation of the "naked"
eye. One needs to know how the eye, which is an instrument of the
human body, really works before one can understand how much of a
reading made by the so-called disinterested observer is to be taken
as real and how much is the result of the instrument of the eye itself.
At this point, some realists attempt to save the instrumentless observer
by inventing *pure sensory data*, which purportedly *really* exist, whatever may be the instrument that produced them. This is certainly
the idea behind the realist's notion that models are "representations
of sensory experience." This rather weird attempt to save the disinterested observer gave rise to such peculiar metaphysics as Bark-
ly's "to be is to be perceived" and the even more fantastic versions
of later English philosophical thought. The Western college boy has
thus been taken through the strangest of mental exercises, speculat-
ing on whether, when a tree falls in the forest, there really is any
noise, or indeed, any tree. None of these speculations has anything to
do with the meaning of the reality of physical science, which is
based entirely on systems of instrumental observation, where "pure
sense" data never occur. The problem of physical science is to identify
what part of the output of these instrumental systems is to be regarded as a description of reality independent of the instrument. The
disinterested observer thus becomes a design part of the system, a
design based on the best available theory of instrumentation. The
effectiveness of the design is measured by our ability to infer the non-
instrumental properties of the observing system's output. By no
stretch of the imagination can one determine *directly* or in terms of
a pure reaction what part of the observation is produced by the instrument and what part is not. Indeed this is the most subtle and difficult problem of all science, and in some sense it could be regarded
not as the beginning but rather as the ultimate aim of science, namely,
to disentangle what the human observer supplies from what Nature
supplies.

Beyond the mechanical aspects of the human observing system
(reaction time, distortions due to light, etc.) is the far more subtle
impact of the observer's emotional life. To maintain the desired

properties of the disinterested observer, it is necessary to guarantee that this emotional life does not inject itself into his reports; but it is naïve to expect that one can remove the danger simply by insisting on a code of behavior. Some knowledge of the emotional life of every observer must be understood to make sure that the observer's world is separable from this other world.

To best succeed in maintaining the role of the disinterested observer, the proper direction of design seems to be one of dehumanizing the observing instrument, for example, by putting more and more of the act of observation into "hardware" such as computers and physical instruments. This choice greatly limits what can be observed. Specifically, it seems to limit the realm of successful science to physical reality. Hence one reaction to the dehumanization of science is familiar enough: If science can construct realistic descriptions in a nonhuman manner, then the way it describes is really inhuman. Whatever the realist may think of this logical fallacy, the humanist's cry of outrage is real enough. Science is only interested in that part of the world that can be described precisely, that is, with a minimum of instrumental interference. But this part of the world is the least human, and from a humanist's point of view, the most boring or the most dangerous. The disinterested observer has become an uninteresting hero, or else a very dangerous one.

Of course the realist may turn a deaf ear to these humanist complaints. His reply is that what the disinterested observer finds is real, however people feel about it. It is the humanist, he says, who is not realistic; if he wants to pretend that atomic power cannot destroy the world, or that evil men do not want to control the world, he can do so. The real fact is that atomic power and evil can destroy us. Many a realist regards science as a game that must be played according to strict rules; the game is separable from the rest of society, and the results of the game are the facts that the rest of society cannot change. His view of the world is pluralistic.

This attitude, however, does not end the argument about whether the disinterested observer is a separable part, that is, a part whose effectiveness can be judged independent of the whole system. There is that very important aspect of the system of science—it must survive. It is the nature of instrumentation to present only approximation; the early realization of this fact gave rise to a theory of errors, for example, the principle that science can only describe reality within a range of error, and that even this range is subject to error, and so on. Also, instrumentation raises more questions than it normally solves, so that even in the area of study of the physical sciences the unknown keeps outdistancing the known. All this implies that science must survive if the disinterested observer and the rest of the enterprise of science are to have any meaning. The point is that, if the system of science makes a choice that will decrease the error of some of its estimates at the price of its own survival, the choice is an incorrect *scientific* choice, no matter how much "knowledge" accrues. A scientific choice must, like all choices, pay due regard to the whole-system objectives. Even if science is a game, it must be sure the game survives, else the game is meaningless. The joyful game player must not be so selfish that he is indifferent to the fate of other, future game players. But guaranteeing the survival of science is no game; it is not separable from the rest of society. Pluralism becomes monism when one worries about eternal survival.

Thus if the scientific community can help to design a world where inquiry survives, but chooses not to, then science is unrealistic in its plans to describe reality. Of course, the scientific community may feel that it has no choice at all because the problem of survival is in other hands, and specifically in the hands of politicians. But it can only know this if it knows the larger world of which science is a part. So the idealist repeats his theme: The current practice of science is science's representation of the whole world in its own system. We have no assurance that this representation is realistic.

Now, though realism from the idealist's point of view is easy to attack, and its hero is easy to make ridiculous, very much the same is the fate of the idealist in the hands of an astute realist. How can one possibly maintain the doctrine that no man is realistic unless he represents in his specific acts all the relevant world of his life, conscious and unconscious, political and apolitical, future and past? The gods could not demand more of themselves. Men have always known how unrealistic it is to aspire to be like gods. To the realist, the

idealist's doctrine amounts to saying that to be realistic one must be
utterly unrealistic.

Thus a model, according to idealism, is supposed to represent in
a part of the system the whole world of the decision maker—what we
call his *life*, both the outer and the inner life. It must represent his
dearest ambition, his politics, his love affairs, his unconscious, his
death. But why stop there? An accurate model should represent besides the life of his world, his friends, enemies, ancestors, and prog-
eny. The idealist's monism is monstrous; the model builder might
as well give up.

To the realist, constraints on system design are like doors to the
outside world; if the designer opens the doors, he allows to enter the
evil spirits of other designs, frighteningly obscure, deeply complex.
The gods with their backs turned let Pandora open the box; the interesting aspect of this myth is not Pandora's curiosity, which was
natural, but the gods' negligence, which was awesome. The gods
gave man the permission to allow all the spirits into his designing, if
he so chooses. And if he so chooses, he invites in the total darkness of
ignorance, as well as evil. And yet idealism goes ahead and accepts
the challenge. Its aim is to try to bring all that is relevant to consciousness, to try to make all that is relevant rational, to try to equate
the rational and the good, to struggle to suppress evil. The hero of
the idealist is the system guarantor. The idealist concocts such a hero,
the guarantor, to take care of all of the unknowns and evils that he
so threateningly permits to come into the conscious mind. The monism
of the old-fashioned idealist implied that the guarantor is *the* ideal,
or *the* God, or *the* Good. This idealist hero must succeed because he
has been rationally defined to do so. To the realist, the idealist's hero
is absurd; not only absurd but downright dangerous. If the idealist
can be so fanciful as to create a system guarantor who acts for the
good of the system *in perpetuo*, why doesn't he also allow his fancy
to create the opposite, the devil incarnate? Since fancy is what now
predominates and not proof, either character can be created if the
mind so wishes, either is as real as the other. Call this devil the great
unknown. It is the creation of the Greek Sceptics, the Stoics, the nineteenth-century Pessimists, and the twentieth-century Humanists. No

idealist has ever been able to show why the reality of the world is not in the hands of the great unknown, of the devil rather than of God.

Of course the idealist tries to show that the beneficent God is the basic reality. In the seventeenth century he defined God as that entity having all attributes of perfection, and on the basis of this tried to create the proof of God's existence. If God is defined in a certain manner, he said, and if His existence can be proved, then the system designer has all the assurance he will ever need that his assumptions, no matter how broad, will never lead him to ultimate evil and deception.

But a century later the intellectual world had accepted, virtually irrevocably, that the existence of God could not be proved in the manner that the optimists of the seventeenth century thought. Kant in his deep analysis recognized that the idealist could not have his hero, his God, without making what Kant called the *basic postulates* of the world as an ethical system. This was certainly a great contribution to idealism, for it pointed to the fundamental problem of system design, namely, ascertaining just what assumptions about the whole system are required to be assured that there is progress in the system. Kant's basic assumptions were that rational design is possible, that systems will survive, and that there is a guarantee that continuous effort to act morally will converge with system improvement in reality. These are of course not arbitrary assumptions on Kant's part. From Kant's point of view the idealist must accept these assumptions if evaluation of an ethical sort is to be possible at all. This is a quite different meaning from assumption making in modern-day axiomatic theory where the assumptions are the sort of demand that players of games impose on each other in terms of rules: If you don't like the rules, you can go home. No such arbitrary choice lies behind Kant's postulates: If you don't like postulating God's existence, you can't even speak about good and evil.

But the realist of the nineteenth century found Kant's method of postulating the guarantor of systems unsatisfactory. It's true that certain idealists like Hegel tried to find in what they called the *process of reality* the ending point which was an absolute mind and in a sense is a substitute for Kant's type of system guarantor.

But for the realist all this speculation of Kant's and Hegel's amounts to nothing at all, simply because it is speculation. If there is any process in reality it must be found in the facts of reality, that is, in the material that makes up the real world. Thus both Communist and non-Communist historian and economist sought to find in the facts of reality the kind of process that was actually going on. Impressed by the success of evolutionism in biology, the realist hoped to find in the patterns of human social systems the evolution of social forms and thereby judge the ultimate fate of social systems. But here the realist was carried beyond his own capabilities. To get beyond what he considered to be the facts of the case, he had to make vast theoretical leaps. Other realists could only see in the theoretical leaps the old spectre of idealism and hence were led to an immense scepticism about the projections offered by the social and economic theorists.

To the realist it seems that idealism only makes sense in terms of its basic evidence. Where it jumps to after it's stated its evidence is something else again, an unreality that has no philosophical significance. In other words, says the realist, the only meaning that lies in idealism is its adherence to hard, unalterable fact.

Thus our argument seems always to take us back to the same point. Try as hard as we can to develop a distinction between realism and idealism based on historical thought, the two seem to merge as thought presses on. The realist turns into idealist, and the idealist into realist every time we press him to make his arguments clear about his general notions of systems.

Well then, if the idealist and the realist are hard to keep distinct, why should we not just regard them as indistinguishable? If, in deeper analysis, the short-range activist is no different from the long-range planner, then why not say that they are indistinguishable, that is, that they are in effect the same individual?

Why not say, in fact, that the idealist and the realist are always two aspects of the same thinking process? Why not say that realism and idealism are a process of thinking about the realities of whole systems?

In other words, one cannot tackle the problem of what is real in a system without going through in one's own thinking process the opposition between the real and the ideal. To pursue the matter only in terms of the realist's philosophy is to miss half the story and all the fun, and end in nothing at all. To pursue the matter in idealist terms and look only for the meaning of the whole system is to pursue the matter in emptiness of serious thought, which leads to nothing whatsoever. The way to think about systems is to think about the opposition between realism and idealism. The way to describe what is *actually* going on in a system is to pose the opposite poles of the realist and the idealist description. For every fact of the realist there must also be the idea of the idealist.

With this in mind, let us take a look at a theory of truth or, as philosophers would call it, a theory of evidence. From the manager's point of view, a theory of evidence is a theory of information, specifically a theory of management information.

How shall we think about an information system? Well, we can let our thinking begin with realism and its thought that a system should be considered in terms of its separable parts. Hence, the realist's pluralism says that it's possible to say something accurate about the world without having to know the whole world or without having to prove a guarantor. He believes it is possible to tell the manager what is going on without knowing the whole system with which the manager is concerned. It is possible for the scientist to tell what's going on within the laboratory without having to know the entire world. For example, the realist would recall that during the famous Cuban crisis President Kennedy was made aware of the weapon buildup in Cuba. Surely this was a piece of evidence, a fact that stood on its own, and the fact indicated that Kennedy's previous policy with respect to Cuba had been unrealistic. The fact of the weapon buildup showed this to be the case. Hence, for the manager to be realistic, he must take into account the facts. Facts by themselves, therefore, have positive value.

Now we allow an idealist's thought to come in and counter this suggestion. Do the facts have positive value in a separable sense? Can we actually consider the facts without knowing any decision that might be made with respect to the Cuban threat and the way in which Kennedy's decisions will affect other nations or our own national political system? It is therefore not obvious that the fact about the weapon buildup has positive value because the awareness of the facts alone may introduce fatal nonrationalities. The idealist part of ourselves points out that when people acquire facts about juvenile delinquency, communism, homosexuality, and political corruption, they over-react; the awareness produces nonrational behavior. In other words, the existence of a fact cannot be thought about without thinking about the way in which the system will react to it.

Thus the idealist in us leads us to make a distinction between *data* and *information*. A datum is a specific assertion about some property of a state of the world that is *given* in an acceptable form, either to the scientist or to the manager. Information, on the other hand, is some assertion about the world that has positive value for the system designer. The idealist thought is that data or facts can have negative value, but information cannot. Consequently, as we think about information systems and start with the realist notion of collecting "all the facts," we must counter this suggestion with the idealist's notion of the negative value of facts to get a more advanced notion of what an information system is really like. We will not take the simple idea that all the facts in the data bank are to be retrieved and attached to the thinking of the manager or the scientist. The manner of attachment is critical in our understanding of what the information system is like.

The evils of not countering the realist's theory of information and evidence are best illustrated by reference to modern trends toward huge information centers. People want to store in centralized places all that is known about personal health, education records, criminal records, legal codes, science, politics, and God. They want to do this irrespective of how the social system that uses these centers is designed. The enthusiast cannot understand the moral outrage of the opponents of these very "rational" proposals, and accuses them of irrational anxieties, for example, fears about losing their decision-making powers. But the opponents who speak from an idealist philosophy see that, if there is no control on the interpretation of data, the facts will be used to construct wildly unrealistic models which may easily destroy individual men or even the whole of society. This point has been made time and again about the collection of data in the FBI files. Whatever may have been the realist honesty of the inventors of the FBI data base, there can be no question that people have used the data for all kinds of evil purposes, simply because the design of the use of the data has not been thought out well, that is, there has been no counter-idealist argument at work. What is needed at least is a system of legal controls, so that a user of the center cannot simply retrieve the datum "Jones was convicted of burglary." The information, instead, would contain something like an abbreviated model of Jones' life, so that one understands the implications of the assertion about the conviction relative to decision making.

As another example, social science has been dominated by a realist philosophy, an uncritical belief in the disinterested observer. But the idealist's counterthought is that most of social science does not produce information, and that social scientists' claim for objectivity is unwarranted. Social science cannot say that it has acquired such and such bits of information about the real world, independent of decision making, because bits of information do not have a separable existence.

The same remarks apply to the design of scientific inquiry. Wherever realism takes over as a philosophy, then science, physical or social, has a tendency of degenerating into a hopelessly prolonged amassing of data and statistical analyses. This has already occurred in several disciplines of science where computer technology and laboratory technology combined can produce an enormous amount of data and where computerized statistical techniques enable one to run the data through all kinds of fancy analyses. Once the idealist concept of the meaningfulness of the information in terms of system purposes is ignored, then the data monster gets greater and greater and more and more senseless.

Now whereas we have plenty of technology to handle the realist's concept of separate bits of information, we lack the technology that goes along with the idealist's thinking. The point is that we will run into serious systems problems if we simply build large information systems or conduct social research on the basis of the unrealistic philosophy of the realist. It's absolutely essential that we raise to consciousness the realist-idealist debate as we move into an era of large data systems and applied social science.

In this chapter there has been an underlying bias toward idealism if for no other reason than that only an idealist would write such a work. Hopefully, the issues become sharper as we begin to see in what way idealism and realism interact as a kind of dialectic in the design of large systems. Systems designers shall certainly want to heed the realist's demand that whatever is assumed be assumed sparingly, precisely, and with as much evidence as one can garner. The systems designer will certainly want to be feasible and not take enormous steps in the dark. But we shall also want to heed the idealist's demand that we assume consciously what needs to be assumed. We shall want to recognize that when people talk about feasibility, they are talking about an ideal. One does not escape the idealist's demands simply by introducing what appear to be realist terms. If the realist is afraid of looking twenty, fifty, a thousand years ahead, then so much the worse for the realist. If the realist thinks that the past is more clearly recognizable than the future, then this realist thought must be counterbalanced by the opposite thought, namely, that the future is far easier to recognize than the past.

Finally, we also recognize that the realist has the best technology even if he has the weakest philosophy, and that the idealist has the soundest philosophy with the weakest technology. This position characterizes our culture. Whether we want to say, therefore, that our culture is an advanced or a backward one would very much depend on where we are in the dialectical process of thinking about reality.

The thinking man's reply to the challenges to reason has been to construct a debate; whether the debate is an adequate response to the challenge remains to be seen. Part II kept saying that all aspects of the world need to be looked at through different points of view. The next chapter takes up the challenge in a quite different context: not the reality of systems but the aesthetics.

the aesthetics
of large systems

There are several reasons why I should not write a chapter on aesthetics. In the first place, logicians should probably keep away from the topic, because their inclination to categorize deprives the subject of excitement. Second, the *aesthetics of systems* doesn't sound right; the one thing that the beautiful and ugly seem to have nothing to do with is the systematic, and surely the creators of rules and the systems approach paid little attention to the aesthetic. Finally, I have no very good idea about what aesthetics means, despite struggles to read the experts on the subject. I suppose my trouble is that I agree with almost all of them: Aesthetics is play, patternized experience, the contradictoriness of experience, the pleasure-pain of experience, creative nonexperience, and so on.

And yet in an essay devoted to the philosophy of large systems, how can one ignore the aesthetic? Despite my conviction that we don't understand the good and the bad in large systems, there may be some room for doubt: Some people may feel they know that systems are getting better—or worse. But no one with any aesthetic sensibility can deny that large systems are unaesthetic; they are neither beautiful nor interestingly ugly. They are boring, plain, uncreative, abominable, smelly, gray, tasteless. The one thing that is almost universally left out of planning is the aesthetic, despite the fact that city planning often takes place in fine arts departments.

Instead of digging into the roots of the whole elusive subject of aesthetics, I'll merely pick off one little branch: the irritating. Irritation is a suitable topic for this chapter, because large systems are surely irritating, and also because irritation itself is a marvelously paradoxical feeling. Irritation arises out of a feeling of the incompleteness of system design. Of course, in itself, incompleteness is not a sign of the unaesthetic; indeed, some of the most creative pieces of art and literature are incomplete. It is some particular kind of incompleteness that makes large systems so irritatingly unaesthetic.

For example, architects design *efficient* or *functional* buildings. Aided and abetted by audit-minded politicians and bureaucrats, they strip off all the inessentials; the hallways are shiny, straight, evenly marked by doors, windowless, and hopelessly boring and unimaginative. The very least the designers could do, if they had to be so compulsively repetitious in the design, would be to create a rotating gallery of amateur pictures on the monotonous walls. The urge to be modular to save costs is an infuriatingly stupid aspect of the group mind. Hospitals, of course, are the worst of all; they're obviously designed to scare or depress the patient by their efficient sameness.

So much has been said in criticism of freeways that there is no point in trying to create further irritation. But there is something about the construction of a freeway that may provide us with a clue to the source of the irritation. It's that some mind decided to construct a direct pathway across a city, regardless of the consequences. It's as though a man had spent years tending his garden, and his neighbors decided the best way to get to the store was directly across his lawn; they "outvote" him in their collective stupidity.

At a more subtle plane is the unaesthetic quality of our American cities. In large Middle Western urban areas, it's the gray of the day, the sameness of dirt spread everywhere. In some Western cities especially, it's the incredible hodgepodge of patterns made by signs and buildings, stretching for miles of boredom in the bright sun. The gray of the day may not be so unaesthetic as the hodgepodge of signs, because in the latter there is the same stupid, collective idea of making something that serves a direct purpose. Here Everyman builds his pathway to communication any way he chooses.

These irritations of buildings, highways, and signs are all visual. But the philosophy of their design is pervasive. Consider our mass educational system. To educate all students efficiently we must "package the goods" in standard ways, so that the "inputs" can be processed at least cost to society. The very words are irritating; we act as though students were information-processing machines, and as though the job of the teacher is to create a certain type of memory bank in each student. This incredible philosophy of education is continued all the way to the Ph.D. programs, where the students are required to take "qualifying examinations" to test their ability to "output" what was "inputted" earlier. The average undergraduate of a large university probably talks to a faculty member no more than a half-hour a week on any topic. Modern education is direct, economical, and immensely irritating. As direct, economical, and irritating as mass production, mass camping, mass war. The trouble with modern war is that there are so few heroes. The leaders of the troops are all efficiently trained parts of the war machine, and it takes the gigantic efforts of mass media to stir up any national pride in those who "shall return," or those who conquer. Now and then a soldier does something foolishly brave, and we have a glimpse of the aesthetics of war. Modern war is largely the hell of the boredom of captivity; the soldier is either captive of his own army or captive of another.

The irritating quality of mass education, production, communication, is that it's for (against) the masses but never by the masses. It never expresses any more than the single-minded purpose of some mind, the administrator, engineer, entrepreneur, or politician. The most exciting business is small business, the most heroic politics is local politics, but the directness and compulsiveness of large business and large government convert the small enterprise and local government into uncertainty, paternalistic reliance, dull dread.

Large systems are efficient producers of "pet peeves," as many a popular writer has discovered. One of mine is called *social planning*. In modern times, the process of planning proceeds as follows. Some group decides it would like to study a problem of social importance: lack of teachers in grammar schools, threat of revolt of minorities in cities, bad roadways, inadequate information systems, exponential growth of garbage, and so on. They may be motivated to undertake the study by profit, or bureaucratic power considerations, or even a desire to "help."

After talking over the problem together, they begin to write a "proposal." They have to do this, because the source of funds is elsewhere, and the ritual demands that the proposers make a sacrifice at the altar of the givers. The sacrifice is a sheaf of white papers with black hen scratches on them, all bound in a fancy cover. The sacrifice also consists of mental flagellation of a terrible sort, because the proposers must write down in detail what they intend to do and why they intend to do it. Imagine a cook or composer being forced to write a detailed proposal for every meal or composition!

The proposal sacrifice is a supreme example of the unaesthetically dull. It must leave out ambiguity, it must have no humor, no tragedy except an unemotional account of diseconomies, no storytelling except list after list of instances, no pictures except tables and graphs. Above all, no excitement whatsoever at the prospect of conducting the study; indeed, one purpose of the proposal writing is to erase whatever excitement occurred when the idea was first discussed. The last pages of the proposal contain a myth, called the budget. This is a story about how the money will be spent, a story that no one believes (the givers keep assuring the proposers that the budget details can easily be changed, for example, by transferring from something called *supplies and expense* to something called *general assistance*). Above all, this mythical account must be written in the same unimaginative way each time, and the personalities of the story must be replaced by meaningless titles, *senior physicist, junior statistician,* etc.

What follows in the ritual, once the sacrifice is accepted by the givers, is a series of steps called *manning* (never *womaning*), organization, project design, data collection, analysis, report writing, briefing, implementation. Perhaps the most dreadful of these is the briefing. Here the artist is called in at last to make a series of colorful "slides." Each slide must say something direct and simple, to be repeated by the speaker, so that the audience can get it both ways, through their eyes and ears. Above all, the briefing must make the conclusions of the research team appear obviously correct; all counterproposals—including the *status quo*—must seem almost absurd. This task is to be accomplished simply, so that the listening audience is not overstrained in its thinking. Since the briefing is therefore a lie (no recommended policy is ever "simply correct"), it is essential that everyone conduct himself with good manners. The opponents of the recommendation will have plenty of time later on to attack it; during the briefing they usually ask perfunctory questions. About the best that can be said for briefings is that they provide a relaxation from managerial tension; but even so, the shows completely lack any spirit or recreation.

But this is enough name-calling of the choleric mood. It amounts to saying that anyone who regards modern technology as the "leading edge" of social innovation will have to admit that the edge is very dull. In fact, the analogy of a cutting tool reveals the unaesthetic characteristics of modern change—it is change with a singleness of purpose that as it cuts makes a holy mess of everything else worthwhile. Its irritating quality is akin to the irritating behavior of someone who tries to step in line ahead of those who have waited longer: His egoistic determination plays havoc with human dignity. He is irritating just because one sees that in his mind there is no image of an *other*—an opposite of his purpose.

Now aesthetic objects often do have a singleness of purpose—the creation of a mood or a form of a very specific type. It is not the single purpose that makes technology—or rudeness—so unaesthetic. Rather what produces the unaesthetic is the single purpose in an atmosphere where other purposes thrive. Proposal writing and briefings are unaesthetic because, although the situation cries for opposition and debate, these are systematically suppressed. The superhighway is unaesthetic because one can see that the designers decided to pursue one goal in a social atmosphere where opposing goals were begging to be recognized.

But the source of the irritation is deeper than this. Not only has someone pursued a single purpose in an atmosphere of opposing purposes, but we are all led to repeat his act ourselves, over and over. The engineer creates the superhighway over the attractive rooftops, killing the aesthetics of living for the inhabitants below. We follow on his heels, driving with a singleness of purpose ourselves, feeling the enormous convenience, ignoring the opposition of purpose. We repeat what the designers did in the general monotony of affluent living. Whatever plan is successfully implemented in a social system must be relived over and over, so that the stupidities of the plan become the stupidities of those who act it out.

The choleric mood, or complaint, is one side of irritation. It is the side that attracts attention and makes money. If one can complain about bureaucracy, drugs, insecticides, and automobile safety cleverly, he can make his fortune. But the paradox of complaint is all too apparent: It is irritating beyond measure. The most irritating person in a committee is the one who complains about the conduct of the meeting. The students who complain about mass education are immensely irritating to those who govern. That loud complaining voice in the foreign café is sure to be the irritating and irritated American. Even the thoughtful do-gooders who engage in a continuing conversation about social issues of democratic institutions find themselves sinking into the mire of endless complaint.

Complaint is irritating just because it is also single-minded in an atmosphere of many opposing minds. It picks out one defect and drives home its irritation on a single theme. It does not compensate at all, nor try to suggest anything but a puerile remedy. To complain about freeways is to suggest, stupidly and irritatingly, that we get rid of them. To complain of war is to cry for peace at any price. To complain of mass education is to insist with deadpan that we have individual education. All as monotonous as that which is its butt. The irritating patterns of Los Angeles' signs at least have an interest and fascination that the complaints against them lack.

Here is the living action of irritation: a satisfaction drawn from a direct pursuit of a goal, a consequent irritation and complaint, an irritation at the complaint. It's all a part of civilized man's desire to create satisfactory solutions of his large-system problems: Satisfaction breeds irritation, irritation breeds complaint, and more irritation, more desire to be satisfactory, on and on in a circle that will not break.

Will not break, that is, unless it is broken. Some magic is needed here, some mystery, something overwhelming. Sometimes the magic is commonplace humor, the wit that sees through to the ridiculous. Sometimes it is magnificent humor, the wit that displays the universality of the ridiculous. Sometimes the mystery is plain tragedy, a sudden ending of a life of endless torture. Sometimes it is great tragedy, when the meaning of despair is laid bare. Sometimes it is love that breaks the pattern, and substitutes for satisfaction joy and pain. And sometimes, it is religion that does the trick, and puts man in his place—after all.

Can we ever hope to capture, in the design of our new cities and great technologies, some spark that will break through the monotony of our business? Consider the telephone, that remarkable extension of the human ear. How well does it drag us into the monotonous circle of the busy: the direct call that satisfies the caller, irritates the callee, generates complaints about too many calls and too few calls, irritating complaints that must be voiced over the telephone. Could the telephone designers design joy and love and even religion in their marvelous communications technology? Who could ever take such a request seriously? Who could write a proposal for it? Not a telephone that automatically and cheerlessly repeats a prayer, or saves a suicide. But what? A living telephone might help, one that has a mind of its own and is minded not to obey the monotony of human commands. That would be a commonplace type of humor. Or a phone that weeps, or wails "Why did ye die?" That would be a commonplace type of tragedy. A telephone that tells us what we are really like—a psychoanalytic transmitter? Horrors. Imagination can do better than that.

Think what imagination has done with another piece of technology, the building. In Mexico, in villages raging with poverty and dullness of life, there stands the elegant cathedral. How ridiculous! The cathedral is a piece of commonplace humor as well as tragedy. But it is much more—a magnificence that breaks the circle of rational satisfaction completely apart—or does so until the social planners—of religion or economics—bring it back in as an instrument of salvation or education. The ancient Mexicans may have seen further, because they abandoned their great religious cities—perhaps because their magic was in danger of becoming a business.

Would I dare say that the aesthetics of large-scale systems is this magic and mystery that breaks the circle? It's a good story, in any event. But it is also a frightfully impersonal story, while aesthetics always seems to lie so close to the heart of the individual human being. The story lacks a link, a link beween the huge system and the human soul. When someone says "What a beautiful building!" they are expressing something of themselves as they see it in another. Of course, the story I've recounted could be made quite personal. It could say that the magnificent is always a projection of an individual onto something larger and better than his humdrum business of living. But so much more would have to be said about the aesthetics of the individual to make this link to the aesthetic come alive.

But what of the challenge of the last chapter? What has this discussion of aesthetics contributed to the debate? Well, of course, a mood. The phlegmatic has been replaced by the choleric, the choleric by the euphoric. It may be that the irritating singleness of purpose and its counterpart, complaint, are both versions of the realist of the last chapter, while the need for magnificence or just plain decency is another version of the idealist. Each side is portrayed, not in terms of the real and the imaginary, but the aesthetic and nonaesthetic. In the mood of this chapter, it is not a question whether large systems or small subsystems are real, but whether they are beautiful.

The idealist cannot get along without the realist. Also, magnificence cannot exist without irritation grumbling and growling there in its subsystem cage. Without it, the magnificence is an empty shell, an archeological phenomenon, dull and dry and part of some archeologist's business.

Thank God for irritation; thank irritation for God.

war and peace

This part has been a series of exercises in systems thinking, following the prescription of the second part to travel the maximum loop in an apperceptive frame of mind, where mood combines with perception.

When the melancholic and the phlegmatic combine, we get the discourse of the early chapters of the first part. The gist of what they say is that large social systems seem to take on a character of their own. Since *character* is closely tied into morality, the conclusion is that large social systems develop an ethics of their own, an ethics that is independent of the wishes and morality of the individual. Even if we had full knowledge of the good, and full intent to implement our knowledge, we would not know how to go about improving the social system. The do-gooders can only push at the system here and there, and have no way of knowing whether their pushings create more evil than good.

Confronted with the enormous difficulty of creating real improvement in social systems, some will want to shy away from trying to depict the whole system. To be "practical" and "feasible," they tackle specific needs: poverty, crime, disease, and aggression. But for others, all this specific "problem solving" is a mistake. Our law makers and policy formers should be telling us what they think the world is like; the central question of all policy decisions is what the world must be like for *this* to be the optimal social decision.

Kant recognized the need for painting world pictures in his *Critique of Practical Reason.* The greatness of his book lies not in the specific, rather crabbed morality he proposed, but in his posing three questions that all thinkers about social improvement must answer. These are the questions of God, Freedom, and Immortality. They all boil down to one fundamental question: What must the real world be like for man to be able to create improvement in social systems? The sanguine mood of the last chapter of Part I says that there is a way in which the idealist's demand can be brought forward and used to create a new form of rationality. The suggestions of Part II are that we drop the requirement of phlegmatic objectivity, which was the hallmark of classical rationalism: the fixed axioms, the established truths that exist independent of man's moods and wishes. Instead, the rational is to become an interplay of thought, imagination, and mood, necessarily not "consistent" and yet not relativistic and sceptical either.

In this third part there has been a phlegmatic treatment of the real, a choleric look at the aesthetic. To apperceive the good, suppose we introduce another dichotomy of types, the hard and the soft. The hard is direct, forceful, competent; the soft is elusive, nondirected, weak, and incompetent. The distinction is familiar to scientists. Physics and mathematics are hard sciences, sociology is soft; economics has fought the battle and hard mathematical economics seems to be winning. The soft scientists are storytellers; they tell us stories about the world, its past, its present, and sometimes its future.

Among the softest of the intellectual disciplines are metaphysics, theology, cosmology, history, and analytic psychology. All these are soft in their orientation, because they struggle to see enough of the hidden in the whole system to make some judgment about it. But what has often happened to them is that they have struggled to become harder, by accepting an isolation from the reality of the whole system. The metaphysician may be interested in what is real and what is unreal, but his stories are totally irrelevant for the hard decision makers who must act today. The theologician's concepts of God have no impact on the policies of the programs of the Great Society. The cosmologist thinks mainly about the origin and destination of the universe, and not what comes between, which is all that concerns the decision makers. The historian is often the raconteur of segregated past events; what makes him soft is the process of selecting events to talk about, but the basis of his selection is hidden in order to make the historical account become hard fact. And finally the soft psychoanalyst is interested in the self, but not the decision-making self that expresses its inner life in hard outer social change. To become hard, the psychoanalyst must run controlled experiments on his therapy, the results of which say nothing about the psychology of politics.

The reasons for banishing the very soft disciplines from science are "sound" in an era of hard science. The metaphysician's speculations, even if they can be understood, are just that—mere speculation without any evidence. Theology is often tied to the doctrines of organized religion, and in any event there can be no hard evidence for its assertions about a divine being, for His existence, nonexistence, or death. Cosmology does well to confine itself to those areas where some evidence exists; the cosmological meaning of conscious and unconscious life is an issue about which there are no data. Historians do best when they recognize that their function is to record in an interesting way the events that have been written down elsewhere. Psychonalysis, with its quaint and unsubstantiated talk about the unconscious, the id, ego, archetype, or whatnot, can make no claim to theoretical validity.

But nonetheless the soft disciplines are very important and even central to the problem of the improvement of social systems. The "evidence" that something is so must include a world view, a picture of the whole system. The hard scientist's notion of evidence is unrealistic, because it assumes that some datum about the system has meaning independent of what the rest of the system is like. Thus, says the hard scientist, it is a fact that metaphysicians write books, that some theologicians believe in God, that there are several theories of the origin of the universe, that Lincoln was shot in 1865, that many people undergo psychoanalysis. We can know these hard facts, he says, without having to know the whole system, whatever that means.

He is largely indifferent to the questions: *How* do we know these facts and *why* are they relevant? It is enough to say that competent people agree on the data and agree that they are imporant or unimportant. There is no like competence with respect to the flights of fancy of soft metaphysicians, theologians, cosmologists, historians, and psychoanalysts.

Now we can begin to sense another aspect of the debate about social systems. The soft scientist tends to be correct in thought, but he can't get anywhere with his thinking. He has no trouble attacking the hard scientist's notion of competence or expertise; he can easily show that it's grounded in unsubstantiated elitism. But this thought cannot be implemented, because no one is going to pay any attention to it.

Implementation means getting ideas into action. Sometimes it is called technological spin-off, or technological utilization, both phrases connoting the transfer of an idea into practical use: a drug, protective clothing, a new engine, etc. In the field of getting things done, the hard is the politician, the soft the political philosopher. Hard politics is day-to-day decision making, an awareness of what people are like, an astute use of power directed toward specific goals, a competent management. The political philosopher thinks a lot, has trouble keeping up with events, suggests "overall" plans that people resist, talks of global goals, is largely incompetent.

Many a hard politician worries about the fact that "sound" technical ideas are slow in being implemented; many a philosopher is worried about the rapidity with which technology is taking over our social systems.

Recently two political philosophers, Lindblom and Braybrooke, in an attempt to become harder, have introduced the guiding principle of *incrementalism*. The art of incrementalism is to sense those small steps of change that an organization or a society is ready to take, and then to implement just to the degree of the allowable step. The hard politician views with scorn the large-scale planner, with his blueprint of a remodeled city, which no mayor or city council will even understand, and certainly never implement. The soft planner, says the incrementalist, is totally ignorant of politics, and hence suggests large changes that run smack against political pressures. No matter that the soft planner screams in anguish that the "allowable increments" may be irreversible disasters; as always, he is deeper in his thoughts than the superficial but hard politician.

If we apply the interplay of hard and soft to the perception of the good, what results is hard morality versus soft morality. Hard morality exists in the enforceable rules and decisions of legislators and managers: "Thou shalt not exceed the speed limit" or "Thou shalt not smoke marijuana." In hard morality, a violation of the moral code is followed by a specific threat of a sanction, the loss of money, freedom, or head. Soft morality seeks to find the "basic," whole-system morality; its stipulations are general and inevitably vague: "Thou shalt not deprive another of his freedom," or "Thou shalt not exploit thy neighbor." Violation of soft morality's codes is followed by no specific sanction except a hurt conscience; but conscience is just another soft concept that melts away with time.

Nowhere does the drama of hard and soft morality become so prominent as in the arena of war and peace. War is most puzzling to the soft moralist. He sees that there is an international system, and that the manner in which international issues should be settled is in terms of the "whole system." Instead, each nation has its own hard morality and strikes to enforce its morals on what it calls the aggressor nations. What results is puerile behavior, where the boys are playing with bombs. To the moralist, so-called international negotiation is ridiculous if humor is the mood, senseless tragedy if melancholia is the mood; but it's difficult to be sanguine and impossible to be phlegmatic about international politics.

The soft moralist believes that the rational solution of most international problems that threaten war is rather obvious: most problems can be settled by the application of the principle of fairness. The principle says that given limited resources, there is an equitable mode of distributing them. Since the hard morality of international politics largely ignores the rational solution, then the *cause* of war must lie in the narrow and blind attitude of the hard moralists. Indeed, an impetuous, soft moralist might be quite willing to *define* war as a hard moralist's solution to the problems of the international system. War is the single-mindedness in the environment of many purposes that the last chapter described, and hence is ugly. It is incrementalism at its fiercest: Whenever there is the opportunity to change another nation into something this nation thinks is better, we should grasp it and implement our ideas by force "if necessary." And, with a final shrug of scorn, the soft moralist notes that wars are incredibly easy to "implement."

But a soft moralist would go too far in *defining* war in this manner. For one thing, he must recognize that some wars are good, and that many political acts in the international system are not wars. He doesn't want to become a dove with a dove's mentality, repeating the same senseless theme of peace for peace's sake. The doves in their strange way tend to be hard moralists too; they say "Stop the war by unilateral action!" without bothering to spell out the consequences in the whole international system. What the soft moralist means is that war is the act of change—or threatened change—in the international system which is taken without conscious reference to the nature of the whole system. And if this is too general for the hard logician, then he may add the stipulation that the "change" is institutionalized murder.

But in this very manner of defining, soft morality shows its major weakness: It turns introverted and gets involved in its own thinking in order to remain "objective" (phlegmatic). It asks itself, what is the real basis of international morality? Its answer is "the equitable." Thus in its introverted cocoon stage, soft morality comes up with a number of thoughtful answers to the perplexing problem of war. Sometimes it says that the equitable means the removal of need: We must feed the world's populations, clothe them, shelter them, protect them from disease. This thought is a direct descendant of Jeremy Bentham's principle of fairness: the greatest good for the greatest number. To attract the hard politician, one can translate the greatest good into specific economic terms. The prescription then reads: The primary goal of the international system is to provide a real income for each individual that exceeds some minimum (for example, 1,000 U.S.A. 1967 dollars). The idea is that, given the costs of goods and services, one can calculate how much each individual requires to be adequately fed, clothed, sheltered, etc. (To make the prescription still harder, one would have to consider world variations in prices, as well as risks and uncertainties.)

Another thought is to attack the basic unfairness of the present international system: imperialism, exploitation, dictatorship, and the like. This goal may be more primary, because the structure of the international system may be such that Bentham's fairness principle cannot be implemented until the exploitative evil is removed.

Or, on the aesthetic side, the moral prescription may be to create an international culture, beautiful and enduring. The thought is to examine the origins and nature of culture using anthropological findings, to seek criteria for higher and lower cultural structures, and criteria of stability and instability. With these findings, we ought then to plan for a world culture that meets all the requirements of humanism. In this case "fairness to all" becomes one major component of the advanced culture.

Although soft scientists may debate among themselves as to which is the really basic prescription for the international system, the issues all seem to merge into one dominating demand: that we plan consistently for the good of all. Some soft moralists, becoming even more introverted, seek to find an ultimate basis for their findings. Thus Kant's famous *categorical imperative* enjoined every morally motivated will to make the point of one's action a universal law of Nature. This was an attempt to have logic solve the moralist's problem. In an age where logic has become a game, some other foundation has to be found: for example, survival of the species, or creation of a higher species.

But note that all these moral prescriptions of the international system simply ignore one very hard moral law: Thou shalt maximize *national* strength. What has soft morality done with the obvious fact that people believe in enforcing their morals in a hard, specific-and-direct manner? Consider that form of civil war called the *riot*. While the soft moralist is talking about racial equality, the hard moralist is enforcing law and order, payment of rents, payment for food, respect of property rights. The hard morality of the suppressed erupts and reverses all the hard morality of property owners. The latter respond with force. If the soft moralist says that *basically* there is a right way to solve the problem without war, how does he explain the fact that people don't want to do the basically right thing? Of course, he says that people are ignorant and stupid, or that the management of our cities is poor. This is an introvert's way of getting rid of the outside world. In the spirit of his own thoughtfulness, he ought to be asking himself whether the direct, hard approach of war isn't a basic need, as basic as the need for fairness.

Now of course some storytelling soft moralists have done just this, and have gone all the way in deciding that warfare is the dominating influence in the international system. Some see it as a force that operates independently of the wills of individuals, others as a force that ought to operate since it's the only force that can break down entrenched interests that resist progress. But we don't have to make such sweeping generalizations to realize that there is something we might call *masculine* morality, which expresses the need for patriotism, protection of the family and one's own property, and revenge. Any thoughtful plan for the international system that leaves out this need cannot possibly be implemented. Nor can the soft moralist say that if only we can educate people to see the senselessness of war, we can go about solving international problems in a "reasonable" way. Here is where his systems thinking slips a cog: We can't get ourselves in the position of "educating for peace" without having first solved the world's feeding problem, and we can't solve the latter without removing the need for the hard-core morality of each nation.

One criterion of the validity of a story is whether you appreciate it; I can't appreciate the pessimistic story of a determined world or the optimistic story of an enlightened world. The stories that tell us about how man's destiny is in the hands of an indifferent God, or Social Force, or Cosmological Mechanism, or Random Device, are dull and sophomoric, are easy to tell, give you goose pimples, are largely unreflective. So is the story that people are basically fair minded and would behave "rationally" if given the chance. This is the story of those who identify thinking with calculating. They believe in extending the traditional concepts of the hard accountant and auditor to social accounting, in order to gauge the measure of fairness in a society. No doubt this is a good idea, but the story that tells us that men will naturally seek to spread benefits equitably, once they see the fairness of our society, is a weak one. It leaves out one of the most exciting parts of human nature—man's addiction to hard morality, to making his idea of right and wrong a reality.

Nor do I like the economist's classical story of the free market much better. One version of the tale is that all men seek their own good. In other words, hard morality is depicted as being the same as selfishness. The story tells us that in the free marketplace where people can make choices to purchase and sell, and the price of information is zero, the mechanism of exchange will produce an equitable society. Hence, the story concludes, the very implementation of hard morality produces fairness for all, that is, produces soft morality. The trouble is that the plot thickens and sours with time: Given a free market, some astute people will make it less free for others, for example, for the workers. So the less free have to get the government to constrain the more free. The government then gets into the free marketplace, and the story gets very complicated and needs a genius like Keynes to unravel it. It's doubtful whether any version of the free-market story can be appreciated, but in the international system the story doesn't seem to work at all. The reason may very well be that the story's identifying hard morality with selfishness is wrong. One source of energy of international politicians is that they are fighting for their people, and it's hard to appreciate the story that the sole motivation here is imperialistic because each nation believes that its claims will make a better world.

Some will still want to say that the international system is like a national system before law and order are enforceable: Men will fight each other instead of negotiating and bargaining. These storytellers want us to believe that riot and revolution must be eradicated, just as gun slinging was eradicated in the West. Their story, too, is hard to appreciate, because it leaves out one chapter that tells us how men use law and order as instruments of suppression, and negotiation as an exploitative device.

Finally, I don't like the Children's Hour story of good guys and bad guys, which explains riot and war as the product of specially trained instigators. It's a story that is difficult to appreciate because it directly insults the hard morality of the sincere opponent. To be convincing, the story must recount how very flexible are the "masses" in their hard morality, how an inspiring speaker or insidious infiltrator can shape hard morality. It's an undignified story.

I like somewhat better E. A. Singer's fascinating story, which combines the nineteenth-century optimism about progress with the twentieth century's realistic approach to conflict. Singer tells us how man seeks the equitable life, a kind of tripartite existence in which production, science, and cooperation are the goals. Production provides a man with the capabilities of gaining what he wants, and science improves these capabilities. Left to themselves, production and science can destroy us all via more and more efficient wars or other negative technologies. Cooperation becomes the controlling force: Its aim is to make men wish most for those goals that increase other men's powers. This much of the story is sheer optimism; it is the comedy of man's social life characterized best by the term *satisfaction*. But there is another side which erupts when the degree of satisfaction becomes too great. It is the side that perceives the pitiful state of man's "satisfactory life," of a Roman culture, a highly industrialized nation, a high Oriental culture. Its mood is tragic, sometimes violent, always seeking to destroy the foundations of the satisfactory. The inspiration of Singer's story was his account of the history of science, one episode after another when complacency was shattered, by Copernicus, by Newton, by Einstein, by Heisenberg. One "ideal" of progress is to create the "optimal" shatterer of old tablets, a shatterer that does not simultaneously shatter all chance of further progress in the cooperative ideals. Mood plays its part in all this process: The mood of the cooperative ideals is sanguine, phlegmatic, comic; the mood of the shattering ideal is filled with despair and joy, is tragic.

Singer's story is quite soft; it does sweep in something of the spirit of hard morality, but not enough of it. I appreciate it because it doesn't separate out the pieces and relegate all hard morality to evil and ignorance. It has something of the quality of a great novel; the novel seems to be one place where men can tell the stories that we can appreciate. But novel writing is just another example of our social segregation; no one seems to know how to use novels in the management of our affairs.

You can see that I'm hungry for more and better stories from soft morality—not stories that just account for hard morality, but stories that put hard morality into the system. With all the appreciation in the world for what has already been done in the soft disciplines, I've some requests to make.

I want the metaphysician to tell me what the whole system must be like if hard morality is real and permanent, but I won't appreciate his story if he reverts to sophomoric determinism or "randomism." I'd also like him to avoid calling hard morality "evil," because I think good-and-evil is an interplay that occurs in all moralities: Soft morality has its evil side. Finally, I'd like to know how the interplay of hard-and-soft morality relates to the interplay of realist-and-idealist. After all, it's silly to say that all idealists are soft, because sometimes they create wars and revolutions to make sure that their hard idealism is realized.

Of the theologian I want a story of a God whose love is not based on fairness or homespun maternalism. What is the whole system like if there is a God, but He is unfair though still beneficent? (Of course, I realize that the Bible contains some stories of this kind.) I won't appreciate theological stories of agnosticism or atheism, because these, like the tales of determinism and scepticism, are pretty dull stuff. They're made up by people who have been captured and made unreflective by hard reality.

My request of the cosmologist is unreasonable. He has already told us some marvelous tales about the origin and end of the universe, about its size, about the speed with which the universe is expanding. I want a story that explains the morality of such a whole system. A weak version of the story tells us about the significance of morality in a universe where we are a microorganism on a speck of dust flying around a tiny light among billions of lights in a galaxy among zillions of galaxies. This is a weak story, however it comes out, because it fails to tell us that immensity is something of our own making, a part of our own moral creativity. How does it happen that we created the immensity of the universe? What type of morality made us do it? The question is unreasonable, because the harder cosmologists will want to say that the immensity is a *fact* that exists independent of what we feel, or want, or think is right or wrong. Such harder cosmologists, of course, miss the soft point that the factual is as much a creation of the human spirit as is the moral; that there is a way of looking at the factual so that it becomes a product of our morality. Once the cosmologist recognizes this he becomes quite soft, and probably will have to give up some distinction and membership in academies. Which is unreasonable to ask him to do.

My request of the historian is more reasonable. I merely want him to tell me the story of the evolution of morality. How did it happen? Who invented it and why? Are *hard* and *soft* good terms or bad terms in telling the story? What about law and morality? What about teleology and morality? Was Hume right in saying that morality has its basis in social utility? It's a good story, widely appreciated in Western cultures, but largely unappreciated in some other cultures. These are all reasonable requests, because historians already write on such matters.

Finally, from psychoanalysis—or really from any psychological field—I'd like some stories about love. What must the whole system be like if love is a force or an existence in it? What does love mean in a world where hard morality is also a basic psychological need? Can you at one and the same time love your neighbor and want him to take on your morality?

And now altogether: What is war? Account for it, tell us what it is, why it is, what it will be.

Well, if all these and thousands of other requests were satisfied, would we then have met the challenge to reason? Would we then be able to say that by trying very hard in all directions that reflection may point, we had done as well as we can, that no reasonable God could ask more of us? That if we are killed by our own wars, or by the physical or biological universe, we have at least done the best we could? That the ethics of whole systems consists in our thus trying to extend reflection to its ultimate, without any guarantee that it will "work"?

We could say all these things so long as we say them reflectively, which means to ask ourselves why we say them at all. Who is challenging reason? What is the justification of the challenge? I am challenging it in this book, but I surely don't know whether I am justified.

index